PHONICS MINIBOOKS TAKE-HOME STORIES

GRADE 1

PROGRAM AUTHORS
Marilyn Jager Adams
Carl Bereiter
Jan Hirshberg
Valerie Anderson
S. A. Bernier

CONSULTING AUTHORS
Michael Pressley
Marsha Roit
Iva Carruthers
Bill Pinkney

OPEN COURT PUBLISHING COMPANY
CHICAGO AND PERU, ILLINOIS

Cover art by Meg Mclean

Printed in the United States of America.

0-8126-1270-1

10 9 8 7 6 5 4 3 2 1

Contents

About the Phonics Minibooks Take-Home Stories		5–6
Parent Letter		7–8
Minibook 1	The Baby	9–16
Minibook 2	Nan's Family	17–24
Minibook 3	Nat the Crab	25–32
Minibook 4	Sinbad the Pig	33–40
Minibook 5	Panda Band	41–48
Minibook 6	In the Pond	49–56
Minibook 7	Wendell's Pets	57–64
Minibook 8	The Market	65–72
Minibook 9	The Spider Club	73–80
Minibook 10	Eva Uses Her Head	81–88
Minibook 11	Dog Dreams	89–96
Minibook 12	Mail Train	97–104
Minibook 13	The Snow Game	105–112
Minibook 14	The Everybody Club	113–120
Minibook 15	Superhero to the Rescue	121–128
Minibook 16	Mr. Lee	129–136
Minibook 17	Princess Julia	137–144
Minibook 18	How the Rabbit Caught the Tiger	145–152

About the Phonics Minibooks Take-Home Stories

The Phonics Minibooks Take-Home Stories allow your students to apply their knowledge of phonic elements to read simple, engaging texts. Each story reinforces several recently learned phonic elements.

The students can fold and staple the pages of each Phonics Minibooks Take-Home Story to make books of their own to keep and read. We suggest that you keep extra sets of the stories in your classroom for the children to reread.

For a complete discussion of reading the Phonics Minibooks Take-Home Stories with your students, see **Learning Framework Card 6.**

How to Make a Phonics Minibooks Take-Home Story book

1. Tear out the pages you need.

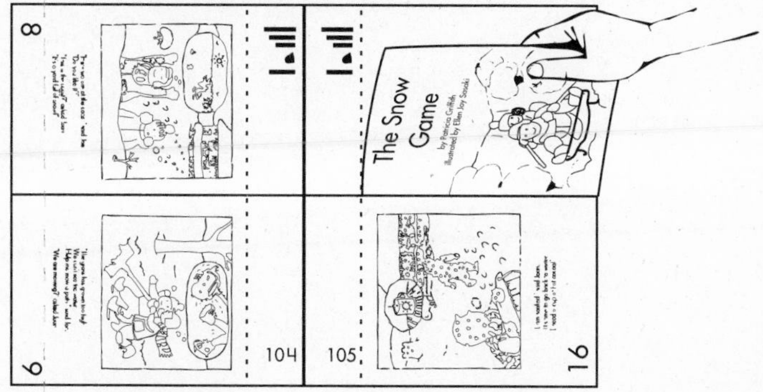

2. Place pages 8 and 9, 6 and 11, 4 and 13, and 2 and 15 face up.

3. Place the pages on top of each other in this order: pages 8 and 9, pages 6 and 11, pages 4 and 13, and pages 2 and 15.

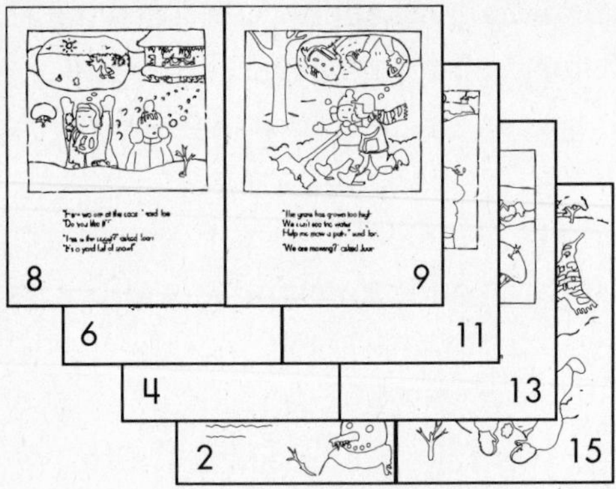

4. Fold along the center line.

5. Check to make sure that the pages are in order.

6. Staple the pages at the staple marks.

Just to let you know . . .

Help your child discover the joy of independent reading with Open Court's *Collections for Young Scholars*. From time to time your child will bring home his or her very own Phonics Minibooks Take-Home Stories to share with you. With your help, these stories can give your child important reading practice and a joyful shared reading experience.

You may want to set aside a few minutes every evening to read these stories together. Here are some suggestions you may find helpful:

- Do not expect your child to read each story perfectly, but concentrate on sharing the book together.
- Participate by doing some of the reading.
- Talk about the stories as you read, give lots of encouragement, and watch as your child becomes more fluent throughout the year!

Learning to read takes lots of practice. Sharing these stories is one way that your child can gain that valuable practice. Encourage your child to keep the Phonics Minibooks Take-Home Stories in a special place. This collection will make a library of books that your child can read and reread. Take the time to listen to your child read from his or her library. Just a few moments of shared reading each day can give your child the confidence needed to excel in reading.

Children who read every day come to think of reading as a pleasant, natural part of life. One way to inspire your child to read is to show that reading is an important part of your life by letting him or her see you reading books, magazines, newspapers, or any other materials. Another good way to show that you value reading is to share a Phonics Minibooks Take-Home Story with your child each day.

Successful reading experiences allow children to be proud of their new-found reading ability. Support your child with interest and enthusiasm about reading. You won't regret it!

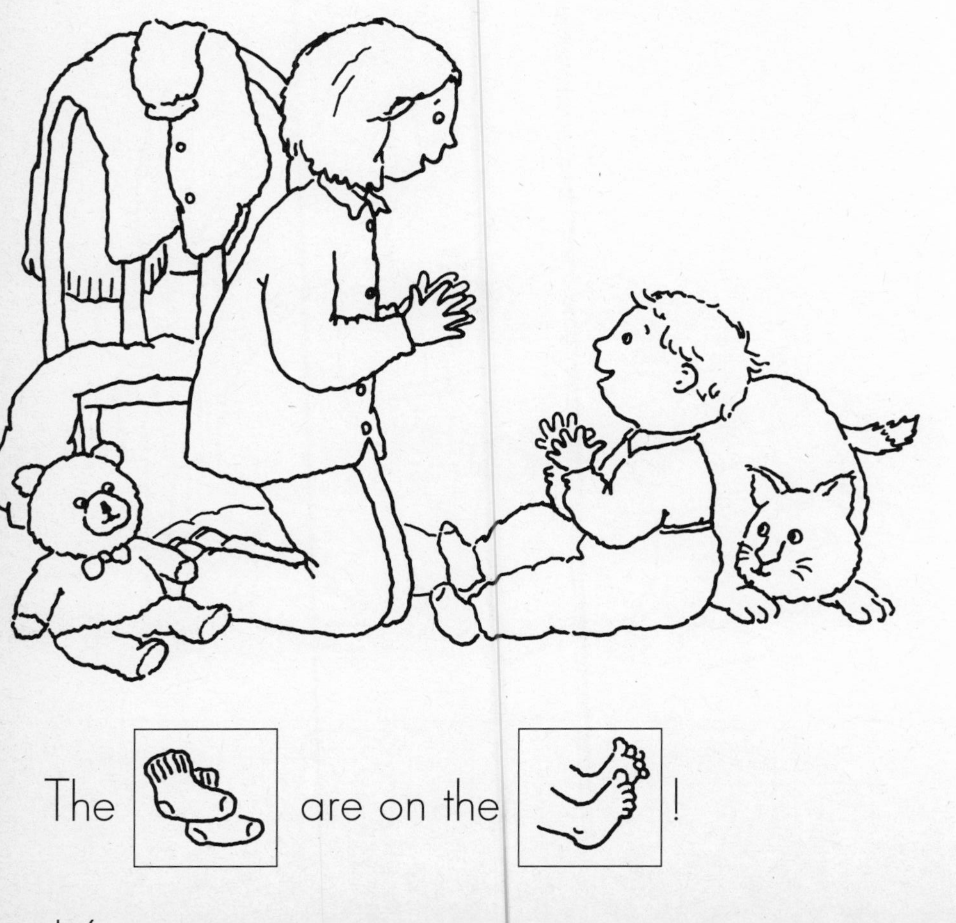

The [socks] are on the [feet]!

Minibook 1

Collections for Young Scholars™

Minibook

The Baby

by Amy Goldman Koss

illustrated by Sylvie Wickstrom

Collections for Young Scholars™

Minibook

10

The [picture] are on the [picture].

The is on the .

Minibook 1

The Cake

The is in the .

The [cake] is on the [ear].

The [socks] are on the [hands].

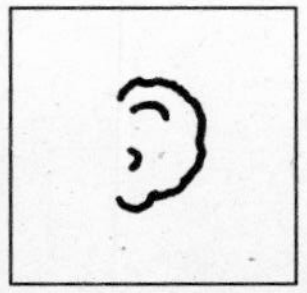

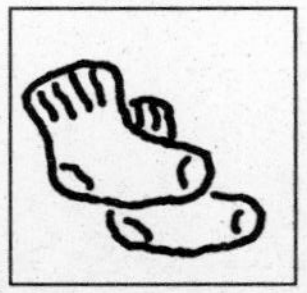

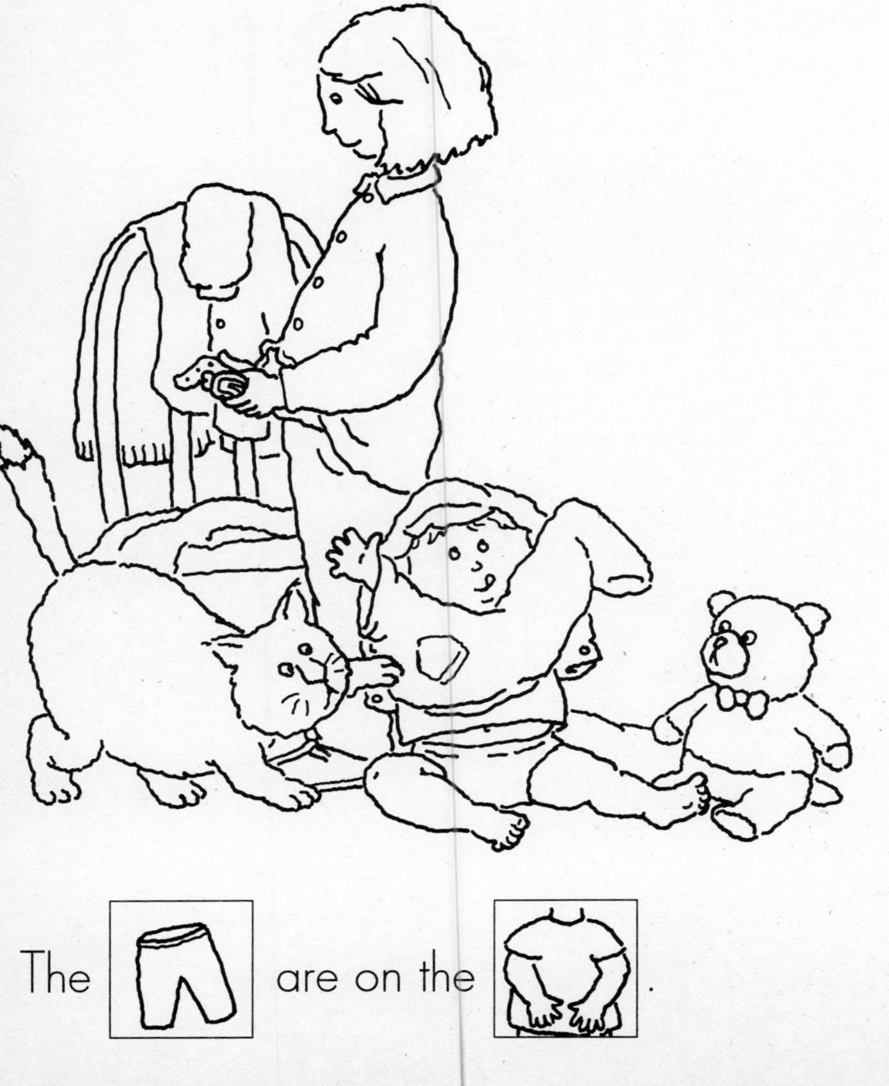

The are on the .

Minibook 1

The is on the .

The  is on the 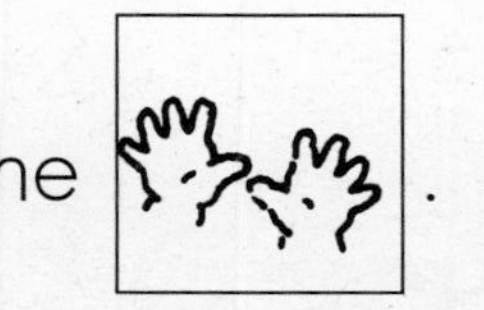.

The Shirt

The  is on the .

Collections for Young Scholars™

Minibook

7

Minibook 1

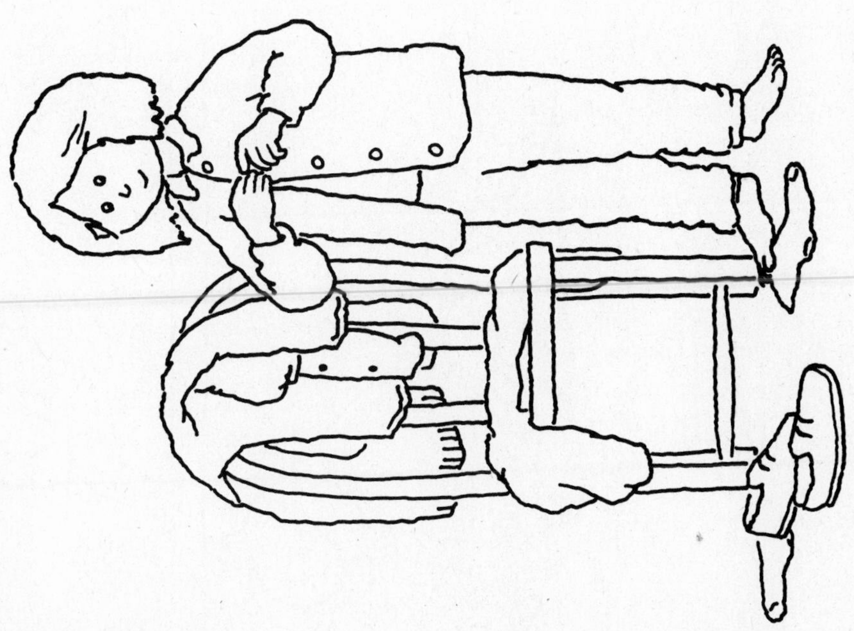

10

The  is on the .

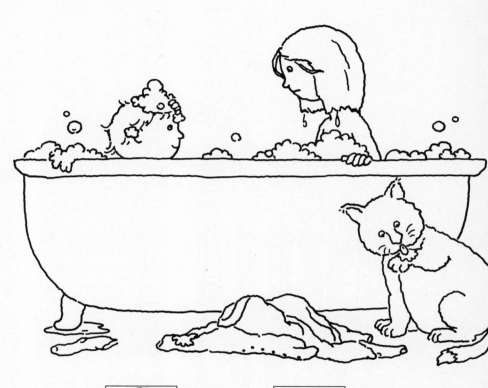

The girl is in the .

The  is in the .

Collections for Young Scholars™

Minibook

Nan's Family

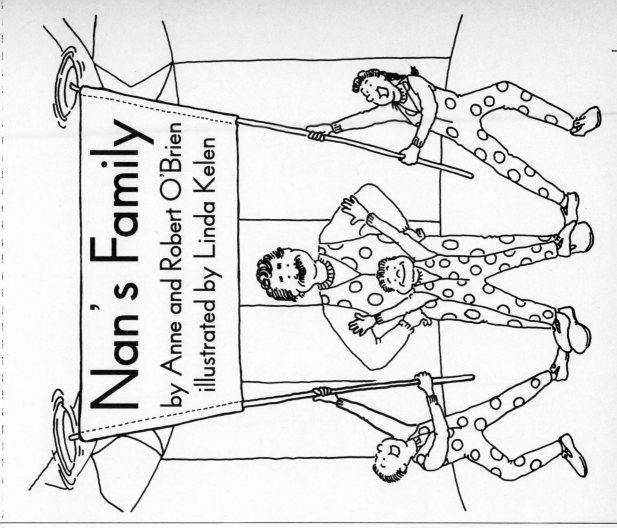

by Anne and Robert O'Brien
illustrated by Linda Kelen

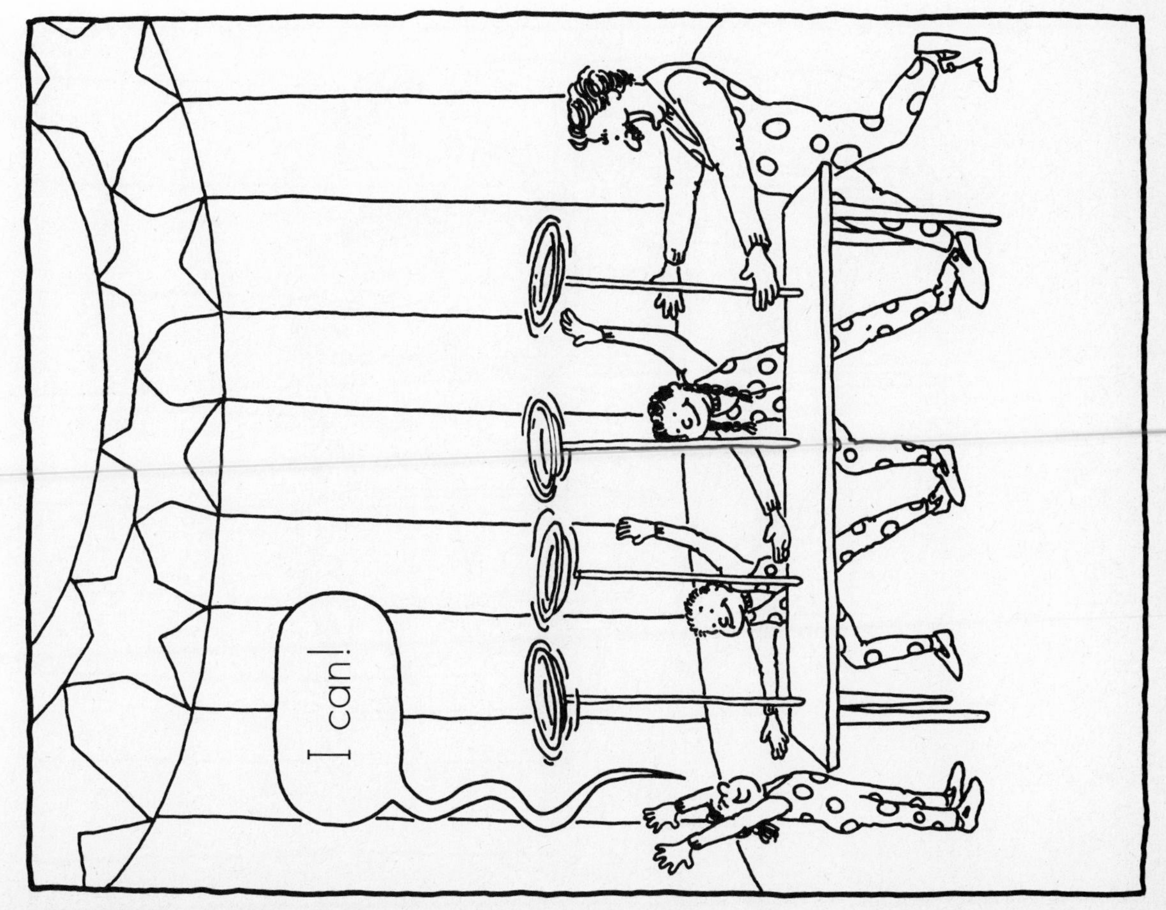

Collections for Young Scholars™

Minibook

18

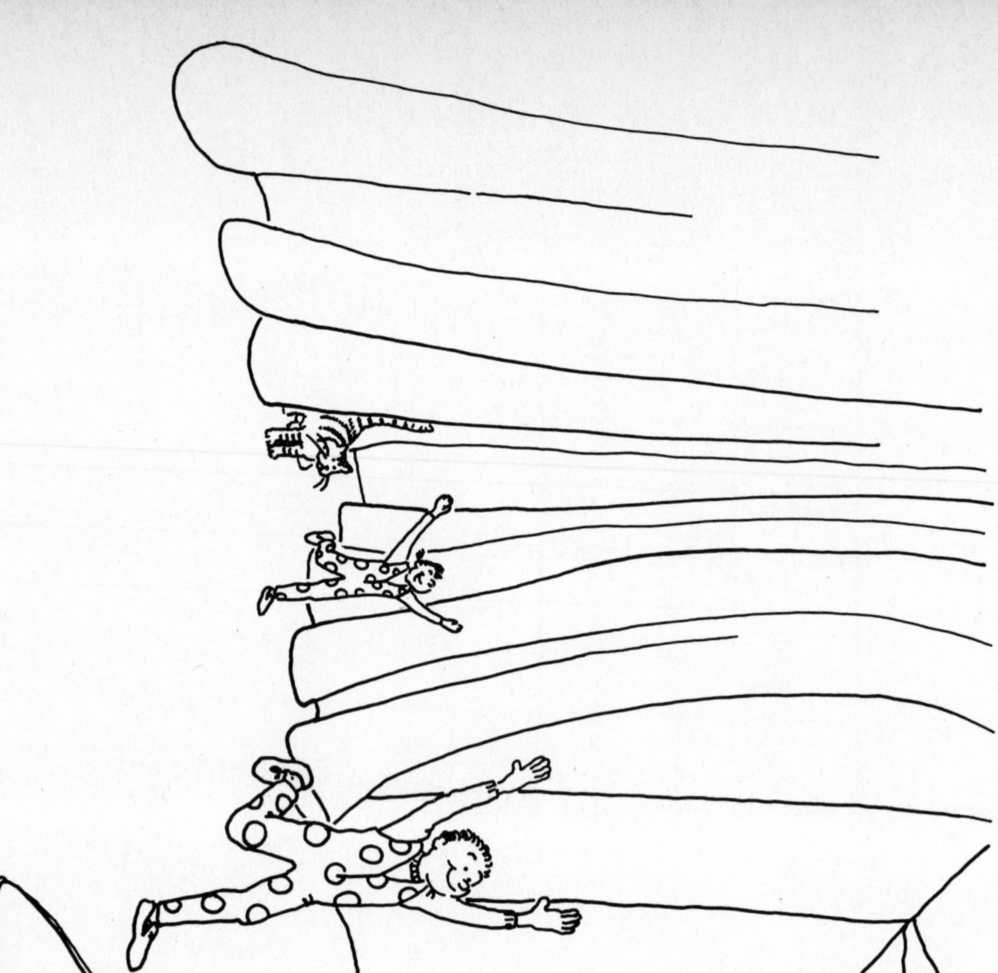

Can Nan tap the pan?

Nan is sad.

Minibook 2

Collections for Young Scholars™
Minibook

On the Mat

Dad sat on the mat.

Pat sat on Dad.

Dan taps the pan.

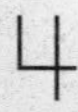

Pat taps the pan.

12

Minibook 2

Collections for Young Scholars™

Minibook

Dan sat on Pat.

5

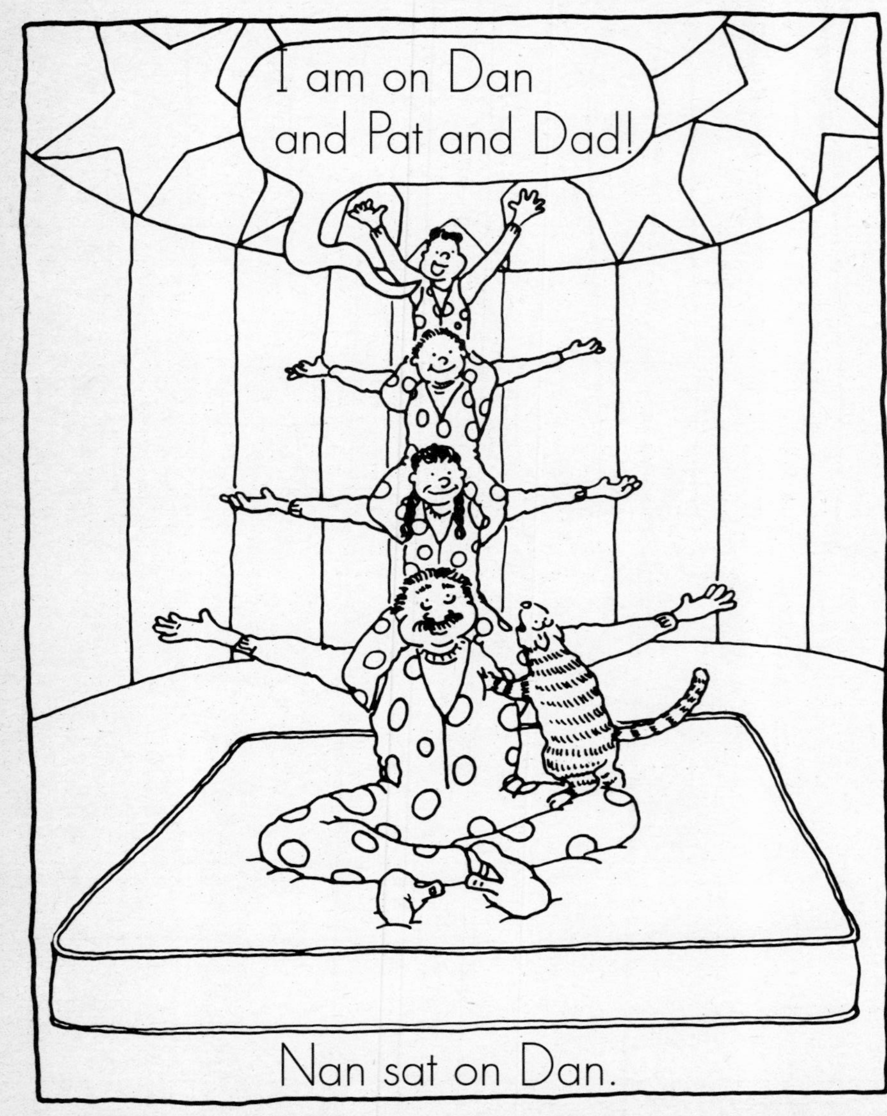

I am on Dan
and Pat and Dad!
Nan sat on Dan.

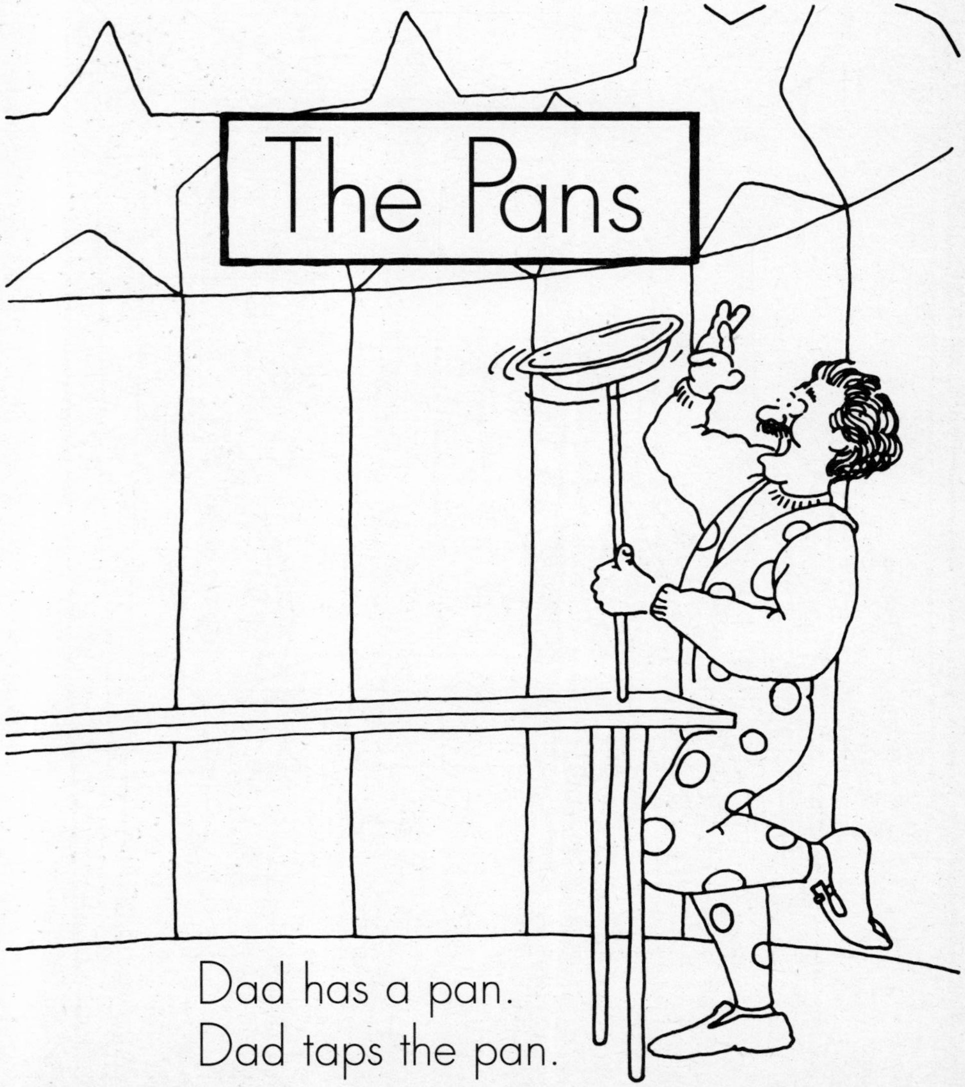

The Pans
Dad has a pan.
Dad taps the pan.

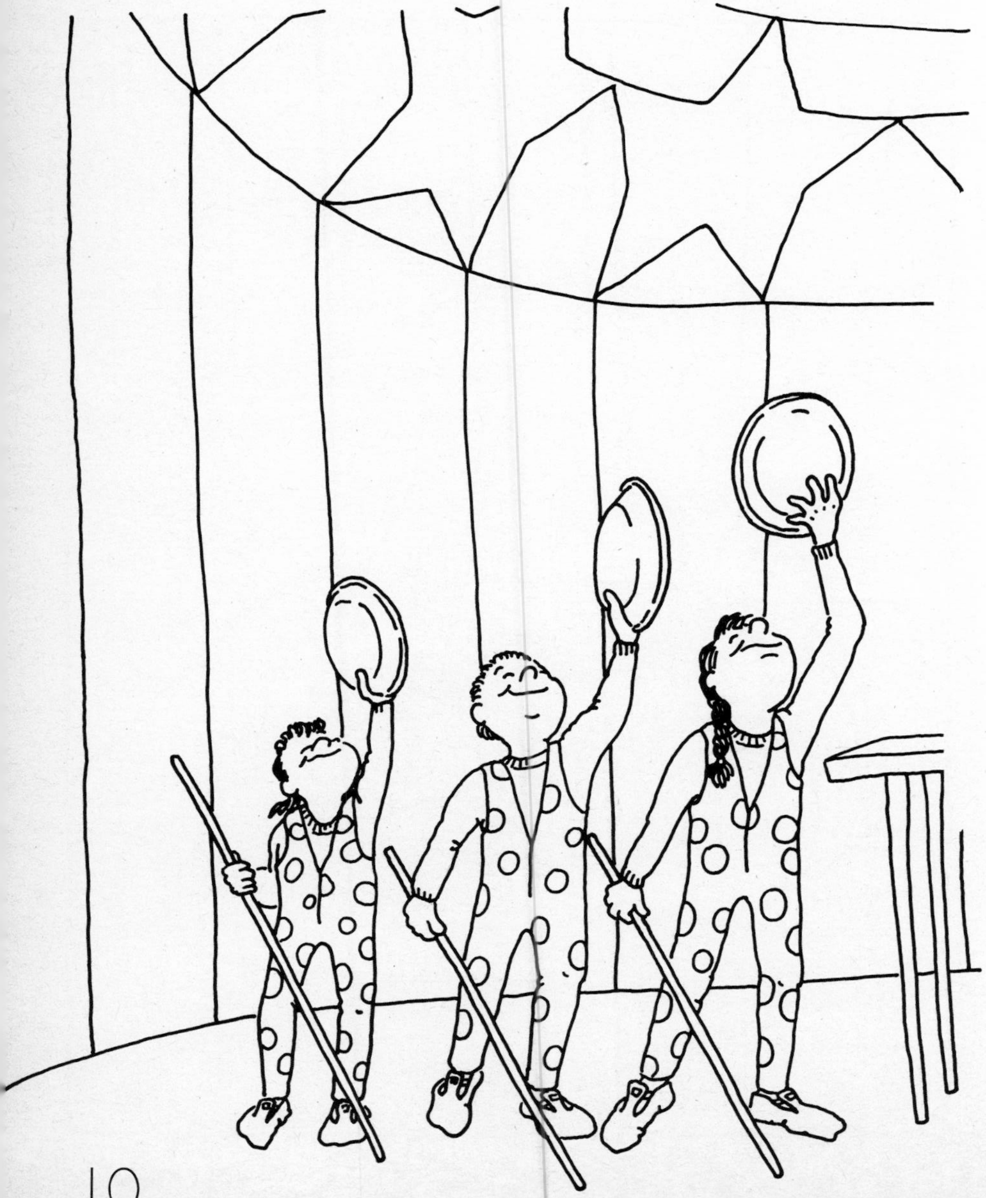

Minibook 2

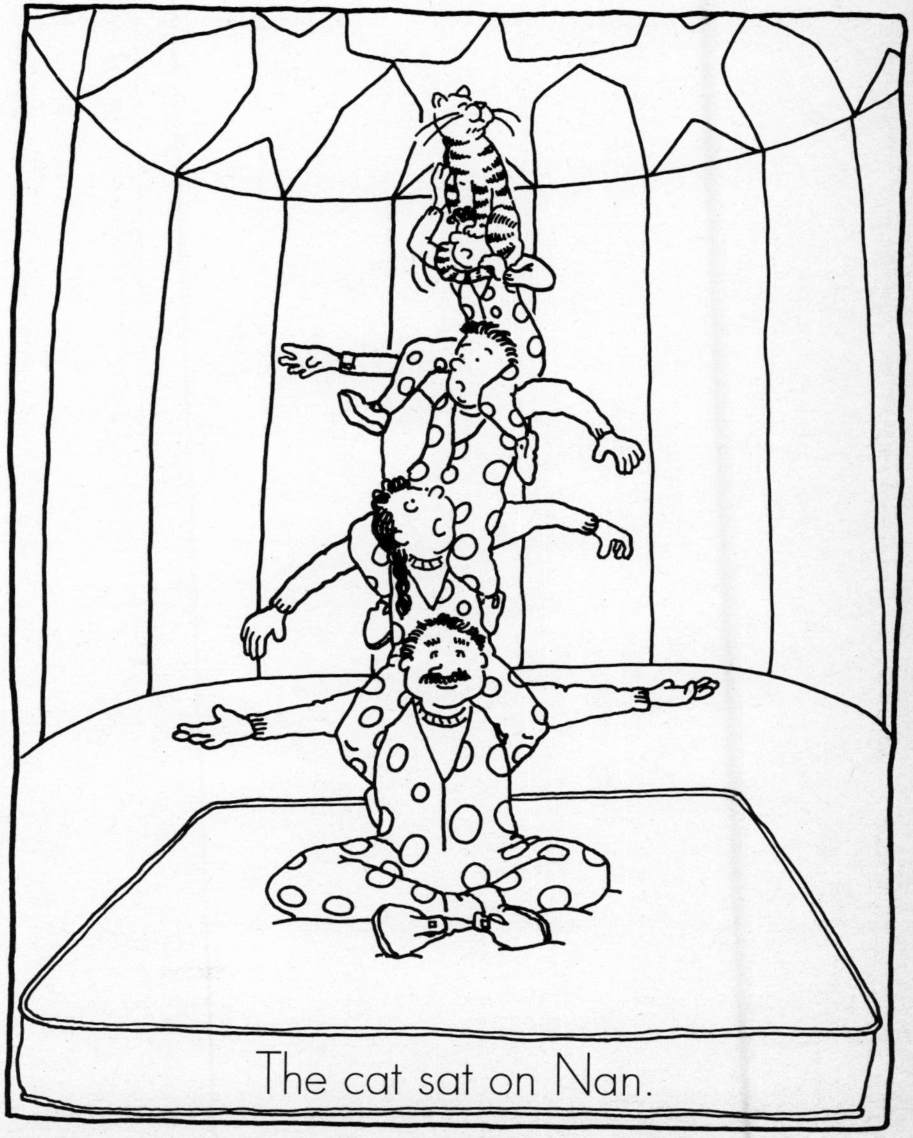

The cat sat on Nan.

Collections for Young Scholars™

Minibook

Collections for Young Scholars™

Minibook

Nat the Crab

by Alice Cary

illustrated by Doug Cushman

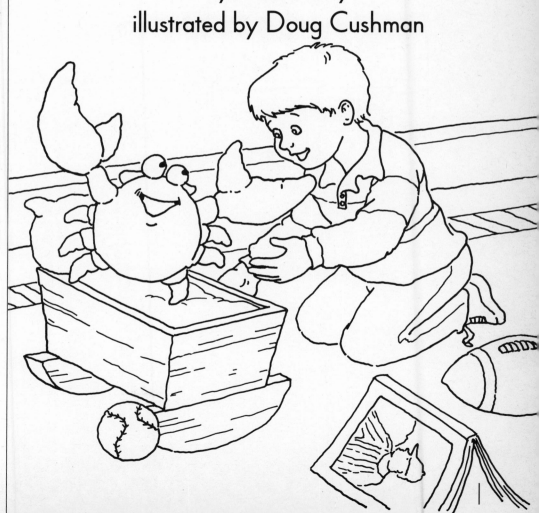

Collections for Young Scholars™

Minibook

26

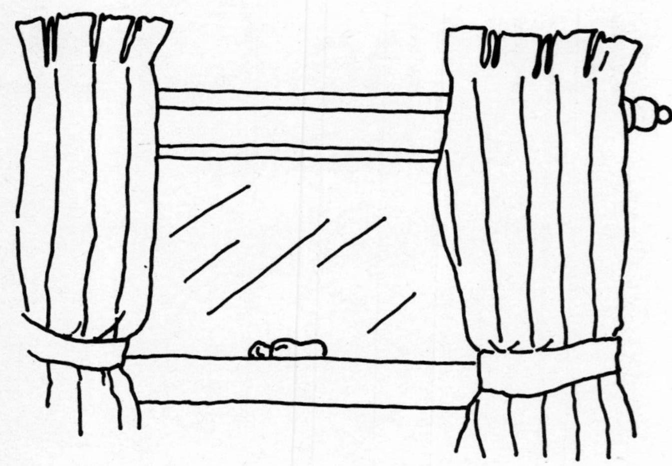

Here is a cap.
And here is a bat.

14

Minibook 3

Collections for Young Scholars™

Minibook

Nat's Nap

3

A crab can't nap!

A trip in a cab, Nat?
I have the map!
TAXI

Minibook 3

Collections for Young Scholars™

Minibook

Nat's Trip

A crab can spin
and spin!

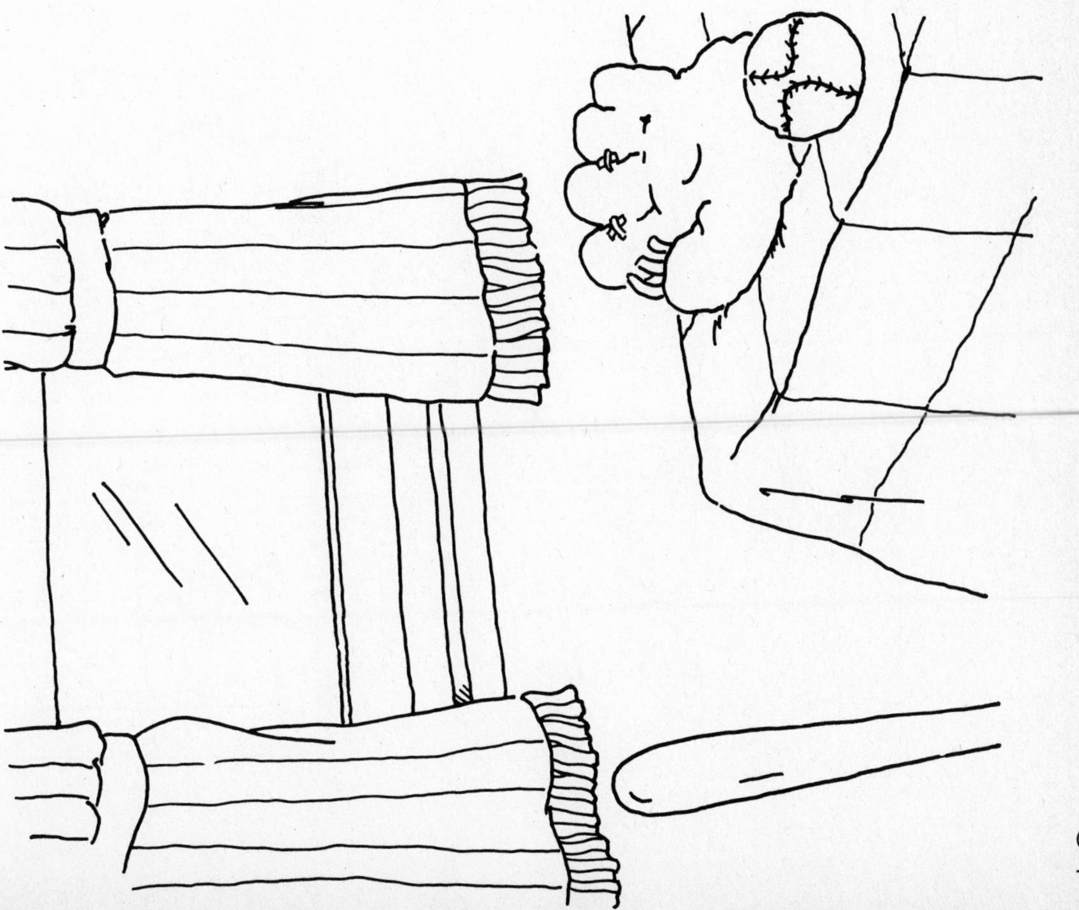

Collections for Young Scholars™

Minibook

A crab can sit a bit.

Nat naps!
NAT

Collections for Young Scholars™

Minibook

Sinbad The Pig

by Anne and Robert O'Brien

illustrated by Meg McLean

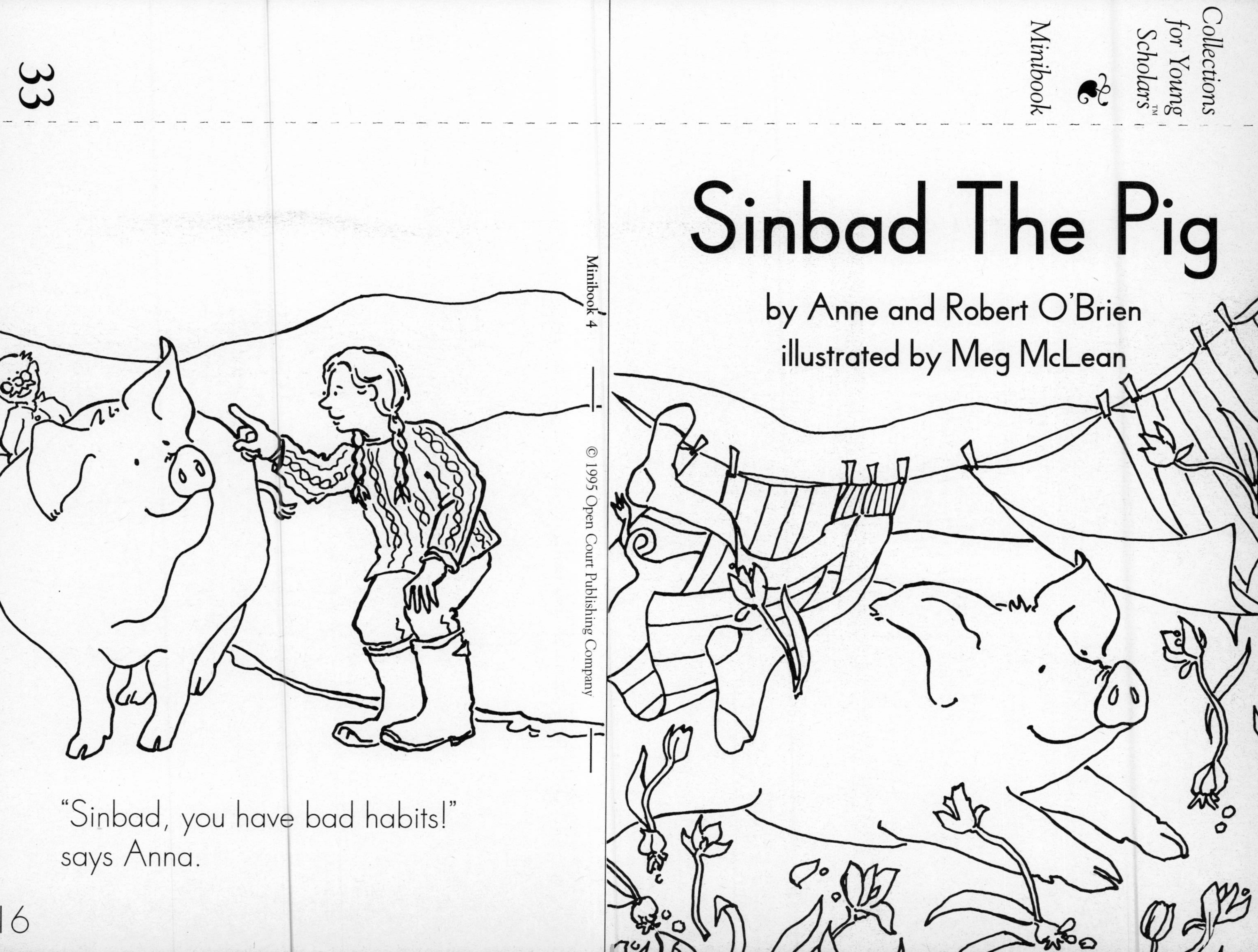

"Sinbad, you have bad habits!" says Anna.

Minibook 4

Collections for Young Scholars™

Minibook

34

Anna stamps.
Gramps grins.

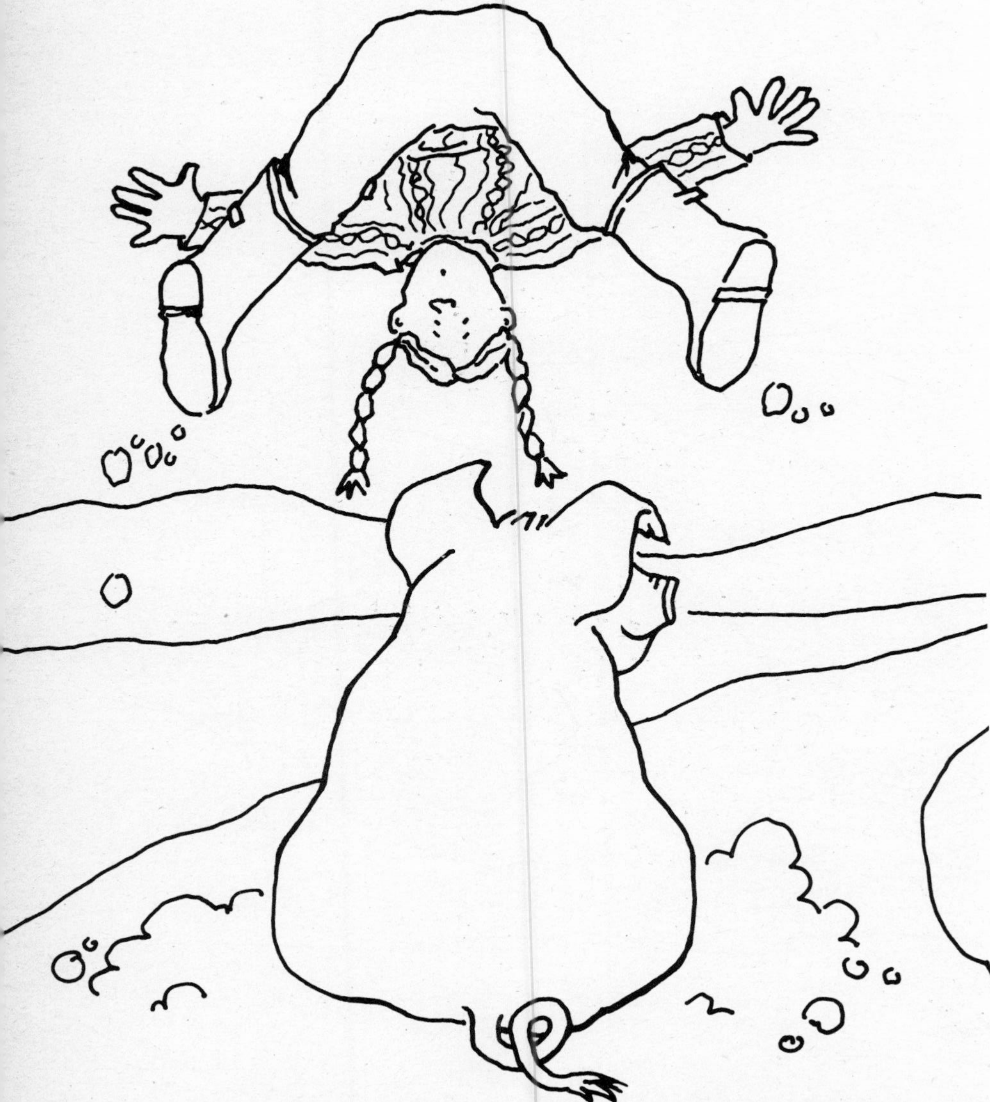

Anna trips on the pig.

Minibook 4

Collections for Young Scholars™

Minibook

Sinbad Acts Fast

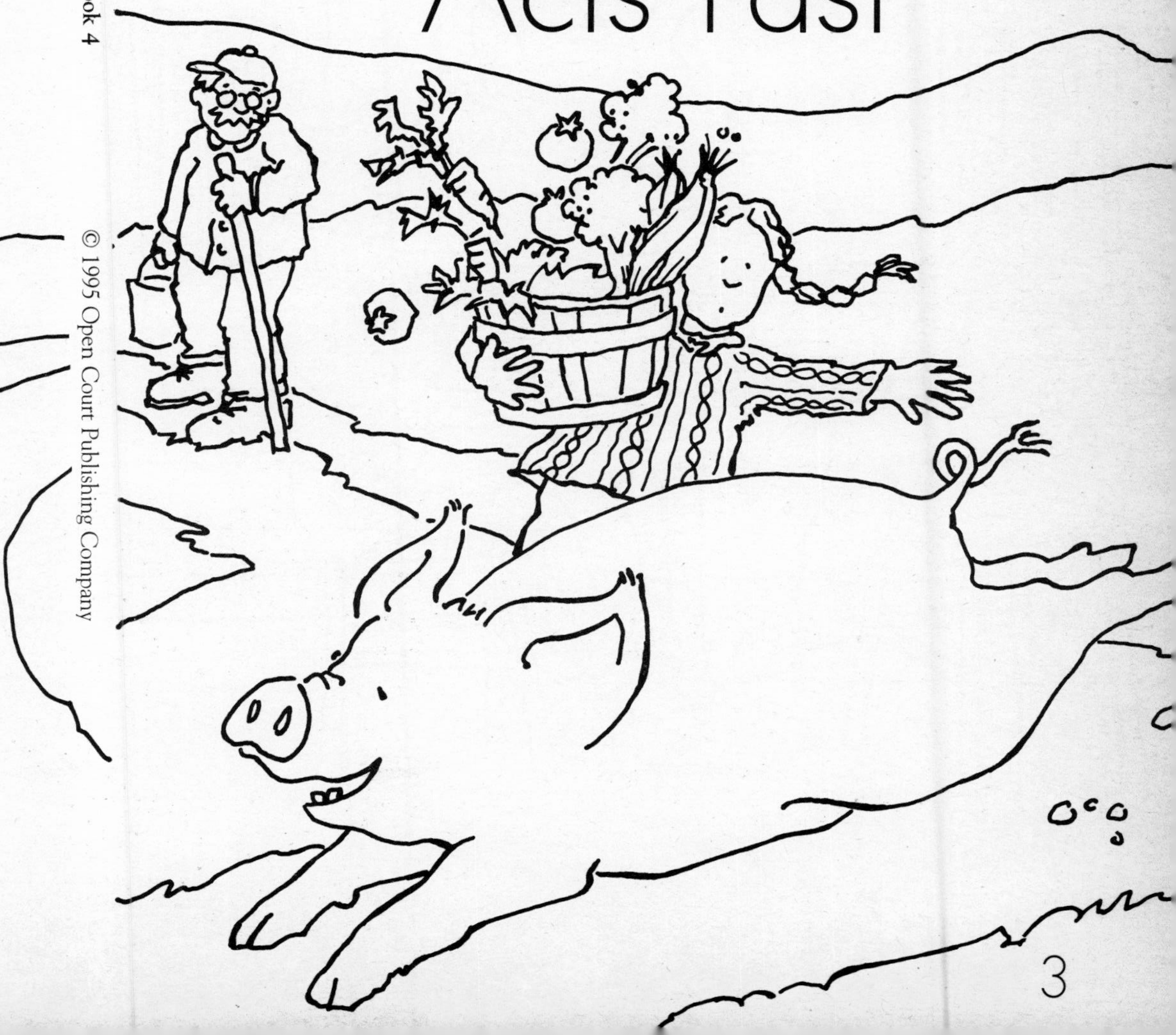

Collections for Young Scholars™

Minibook

36

Gramps and Anna have a big pig.

Sinbad sits.

"I have him!" says Anna.

Minibook 4

The pig is Sinbad.
Sinbad has bad habits.

Sinbad tips Gramps.

Anna grabs at Sinbad.
Gramps grins.

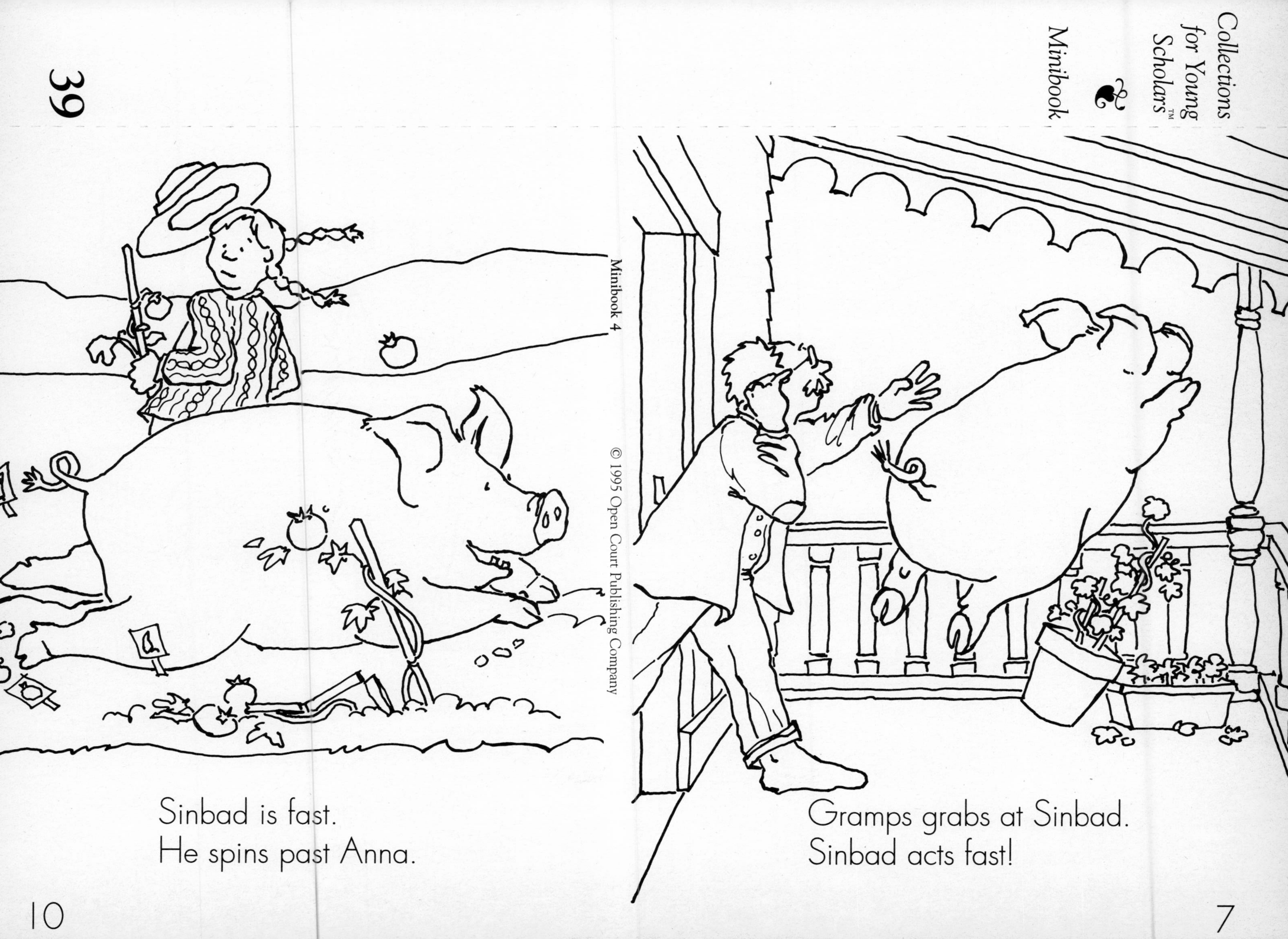

Sinbad is fast.
He spins past Anna.

Gramps grabs at Sinbad.
Sinbad acts fast!

Sinbad and Anna

"Grab the pig, Anna!" says Gramps.

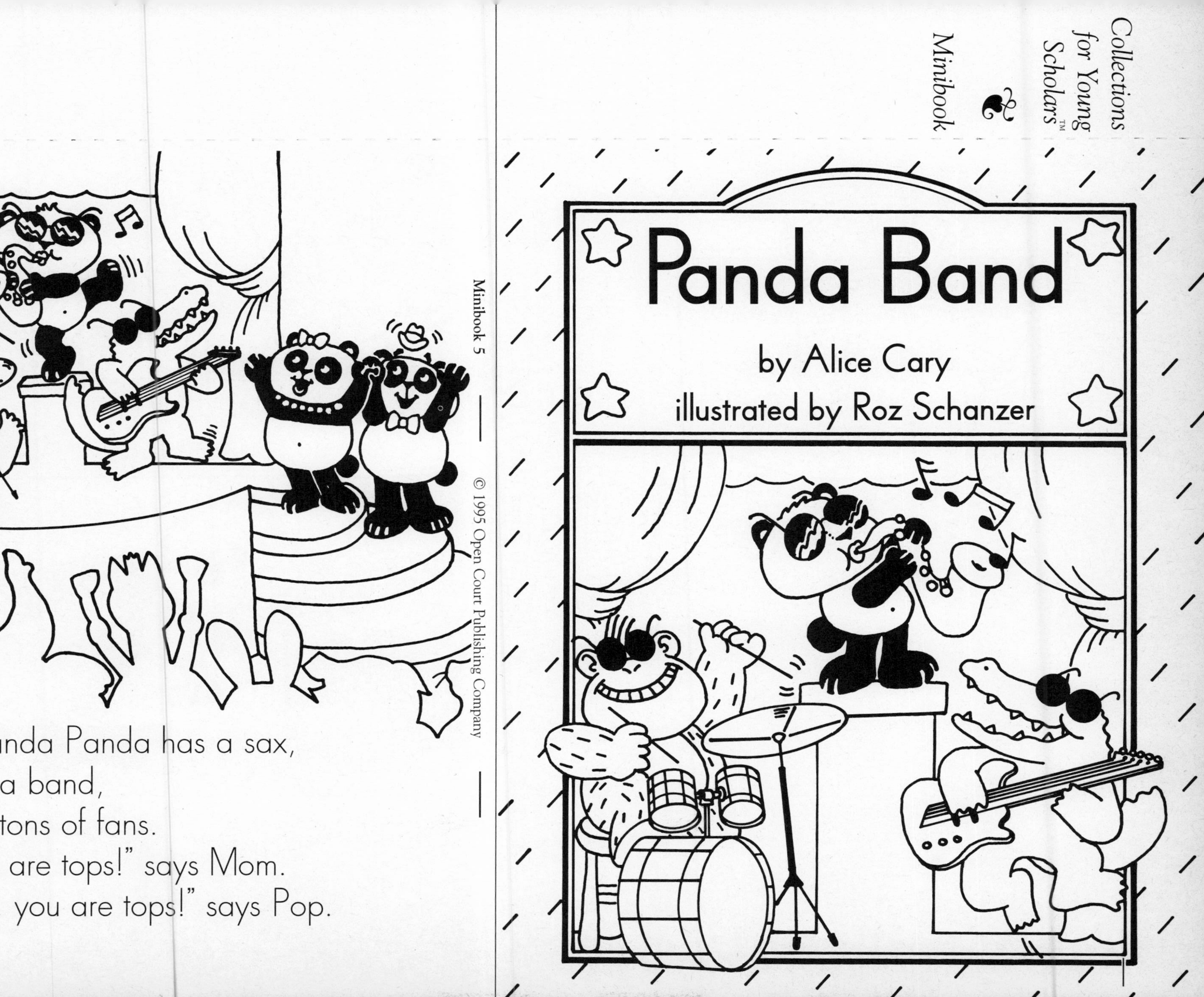

Amanda Panda has a sax,
and a band,
and tons of fans.
"You are tops!" says Mom.
"Yes, you are tops!" says Pop.

Panda Band

by Alice Cary

illustrated by Roz Schanzer

Collections for Young Scholars™

Minibook

JAZZ CLUB

Mac and Max drop in.
"I can have a band!" says Amanda.

"Oh, no!" says Mom.
"Oh, no!" says Pop.

Collections for Young Scholars™

Minibook

Amanda's Sax

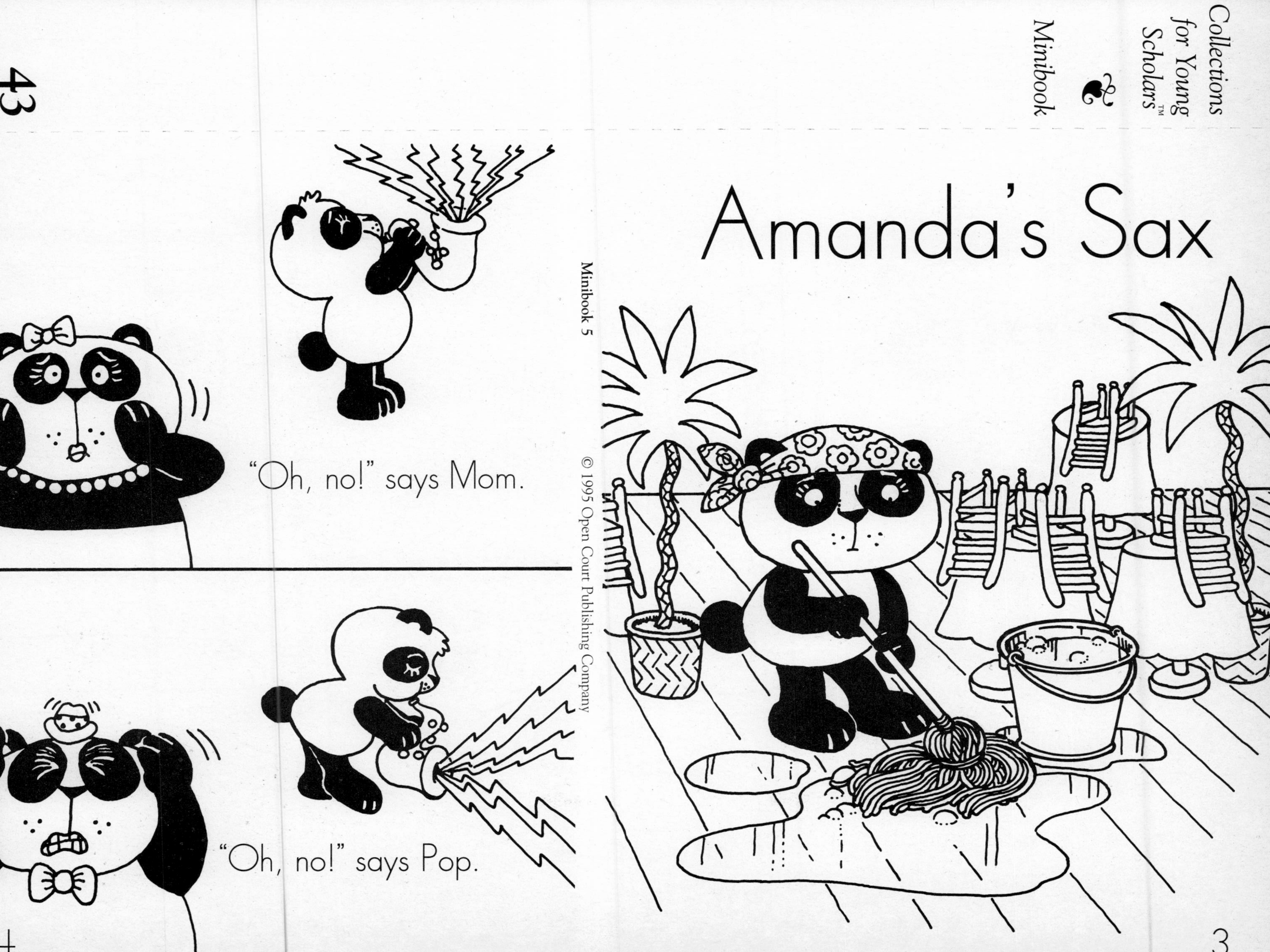

Minibook 5

Amanda Panda mops and mops.
The mop drips. Amanda stops.

"Mom! Pop!" says Amanda.
"I have a sax!"

Amanda's Band

Minibook 5

"I can't stand this," Amanda sobs.

"I am damp and hot!
I have to stop!"

"I have a sax! I am tops!"

“A sax?”
“Yes, a sax!”

Minibook 5

Amanda spots Tom Cat and his sax.

Collections for Young Scholars™

Minibook

48

"You are tops, Tom Cat," says Amanda.
"You have a sax,
and a band,
and tons of fans."

Tom Cat hands Amanda a sax.
"Drop the mop," he says.
"Here, have a sax!"

One hippo in the pond.

Minibook 6

Collections for Young Scholars™

Minibook

In the Pond

by Linda Cave
illustrated by Margot Apple

2

Collections for Young Scholars™

Minibook

50

15

"It is hot," said the five pigs,
four dogs,
three cats, and
two bats.
"It is too hot!"

Minibook 6

"It is hot," said five pigs.
"It is too hot!"

The pigs hopped in the pond.
Five pigs in the pond.

"Not in the pond!" said the three cats.
"Not in the pond!" said the two bats.

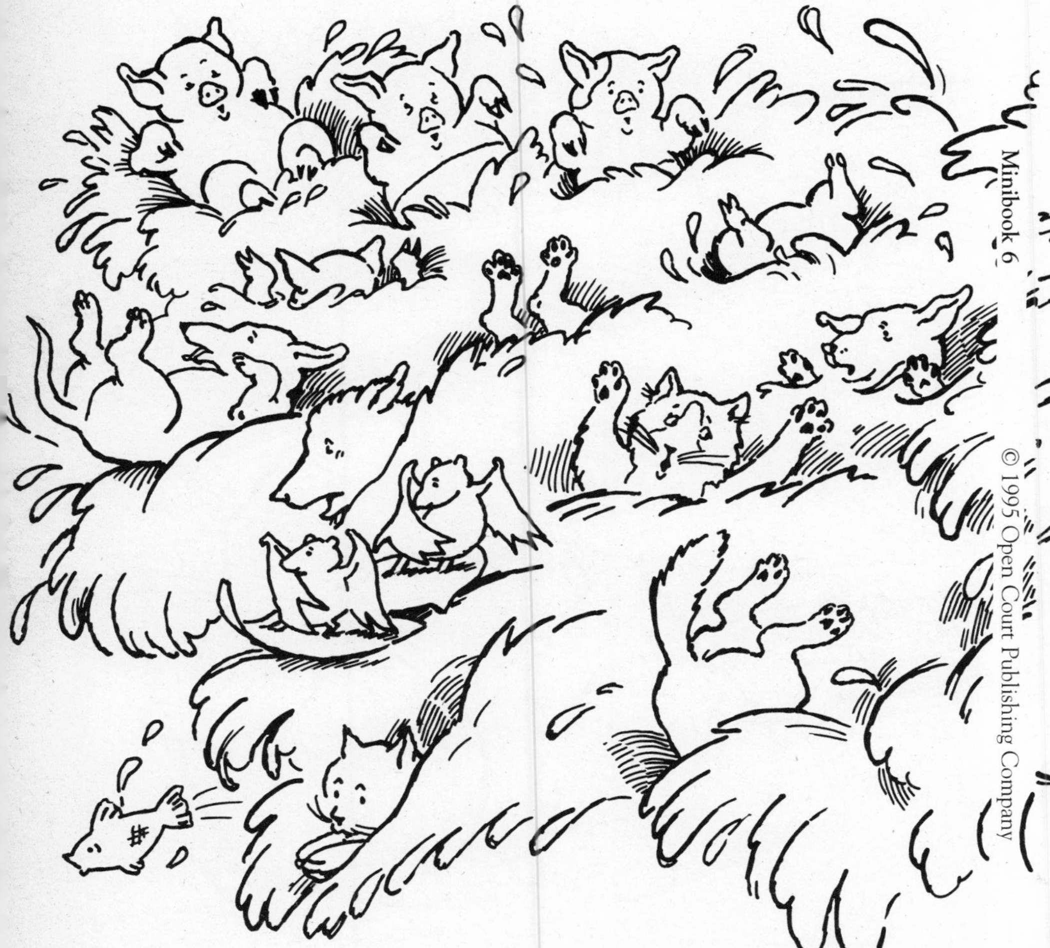

"Not in the pond!" said the five pigs.
"Not in the pond!" said the four dogs.

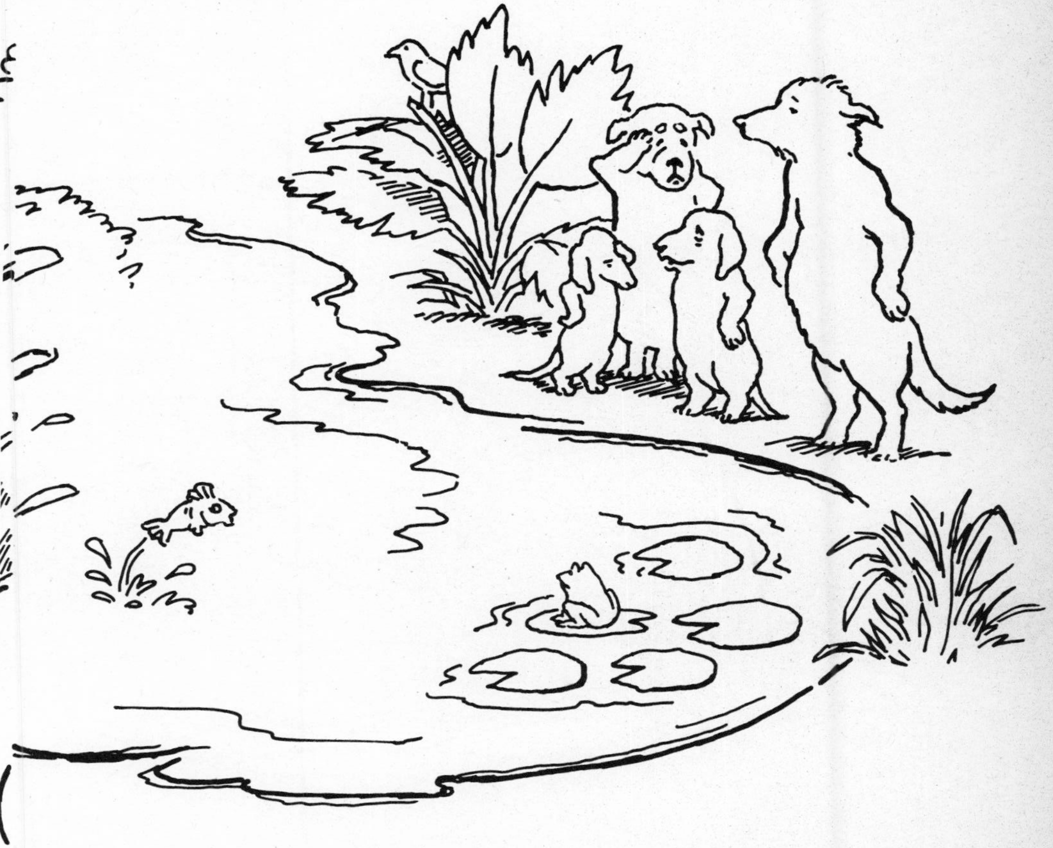

"It is hot," said four dogs.
"It is too hot!"

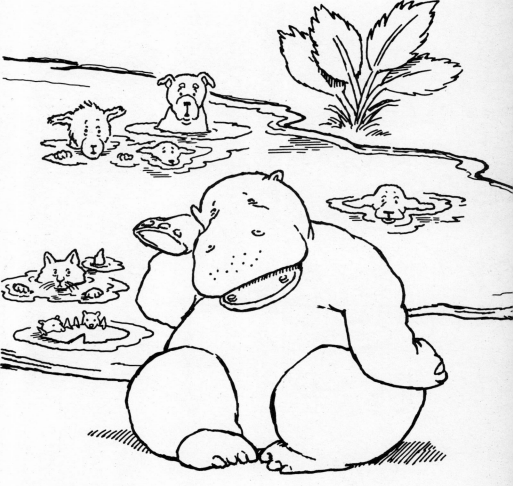

The dogs hopped in the pond.
Five pigs and
four dogs
in the pond.

"It is hot," said one hippo.
"It is too hot!"

The bats hopped in the pond.
Five pigs,
four dogs,
three cats, and
two bats
in the pond.

Minibook 6

"It is hot," said three cats.
"It is too hot!"

The cats hopped in the pond.
Five pigs,
four dogs, and
three cats
in the pond.

"It is hot," said two bats.
"It is too hot!"

"Here!" said Wendell.
"Next to me!"

Minibook 7

Wendell's Pets

by Anne and Robert O'Brien
illustrated by Ellen Joy Sasaki

"Where will you put all the pets, Wendell?"
said Mr. Allen.

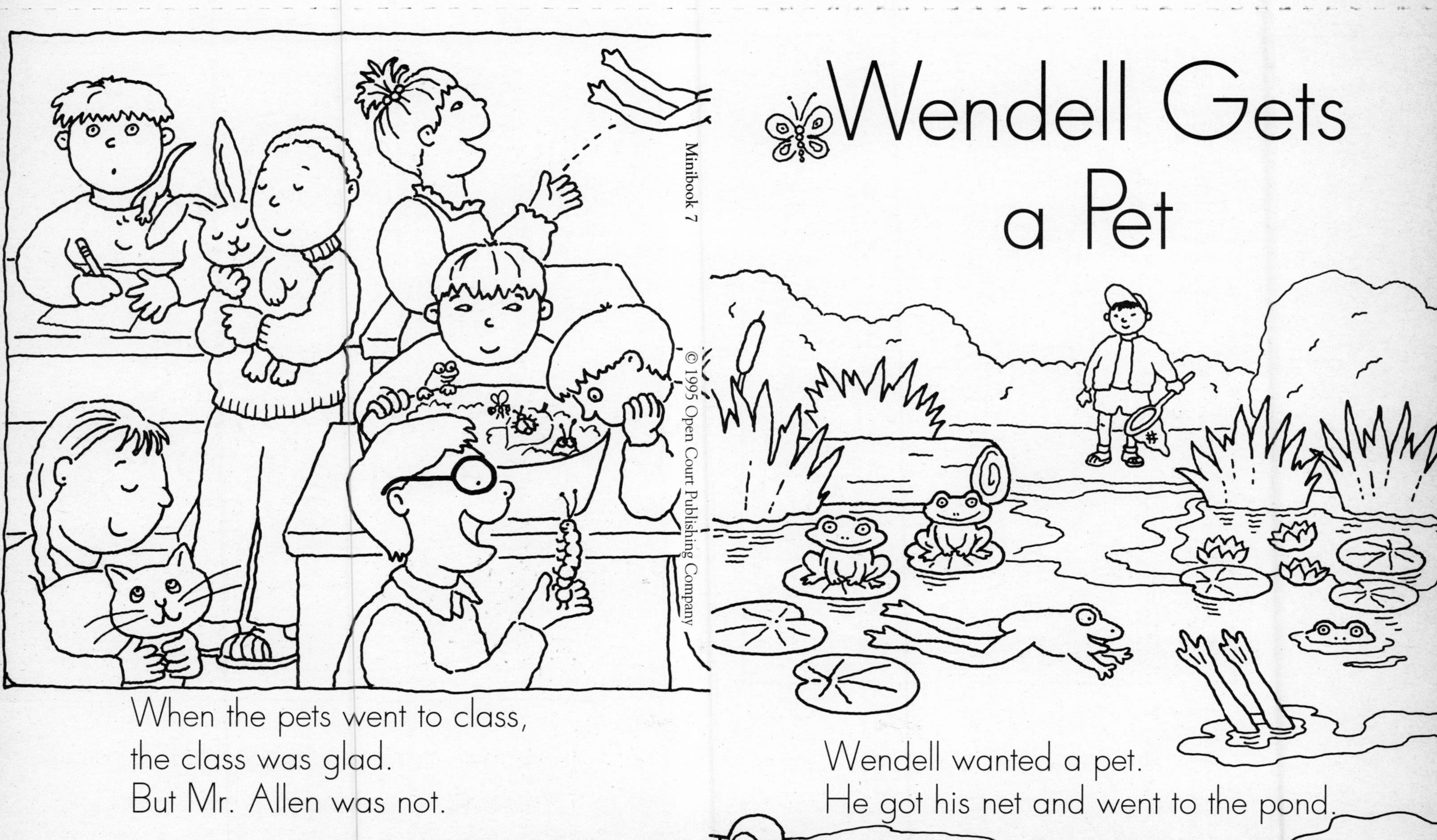

When the pets went to class,
the class was glad.
But Mr. Allen was not.

Minibook 7

Wendell Gets a Pet

Wendell wanted a pet.
He got his net and went to the pond.

Frogs swam in the pond.
One frog was on a pad.

He had a rabbit and a lizard.
He had frogs and a tub of bugs.

Wendell had lots of pets.
He had a cat and a duck.

Minibook 7

Wendell grabbed his net.
He stepped on a log
to get next to the frog.

He dipped his net
into the pond.
The frogs swam away.

Wendell's Pets

Collections for Young Scholars™

Minibook

The log was wet,
and Wendell slipped.

Minibook 7

Wendell fell off the log.
He landed in the pond.
His net fell to the bottom.

Wendell was wet,
but he got lots of pets!

"We can't sell a thing today."

Minibook 8 —

Collections for Young Scholars™

Minibook

The Market

by Marilyn Jager Adams

illustrated by Robert Byrd

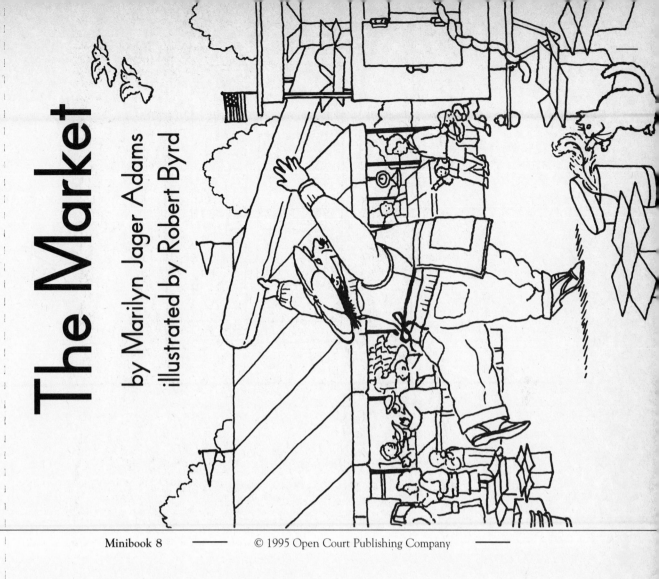

"This lamp is scratched.
It's full of dirt.
I do not want it," said the lad.

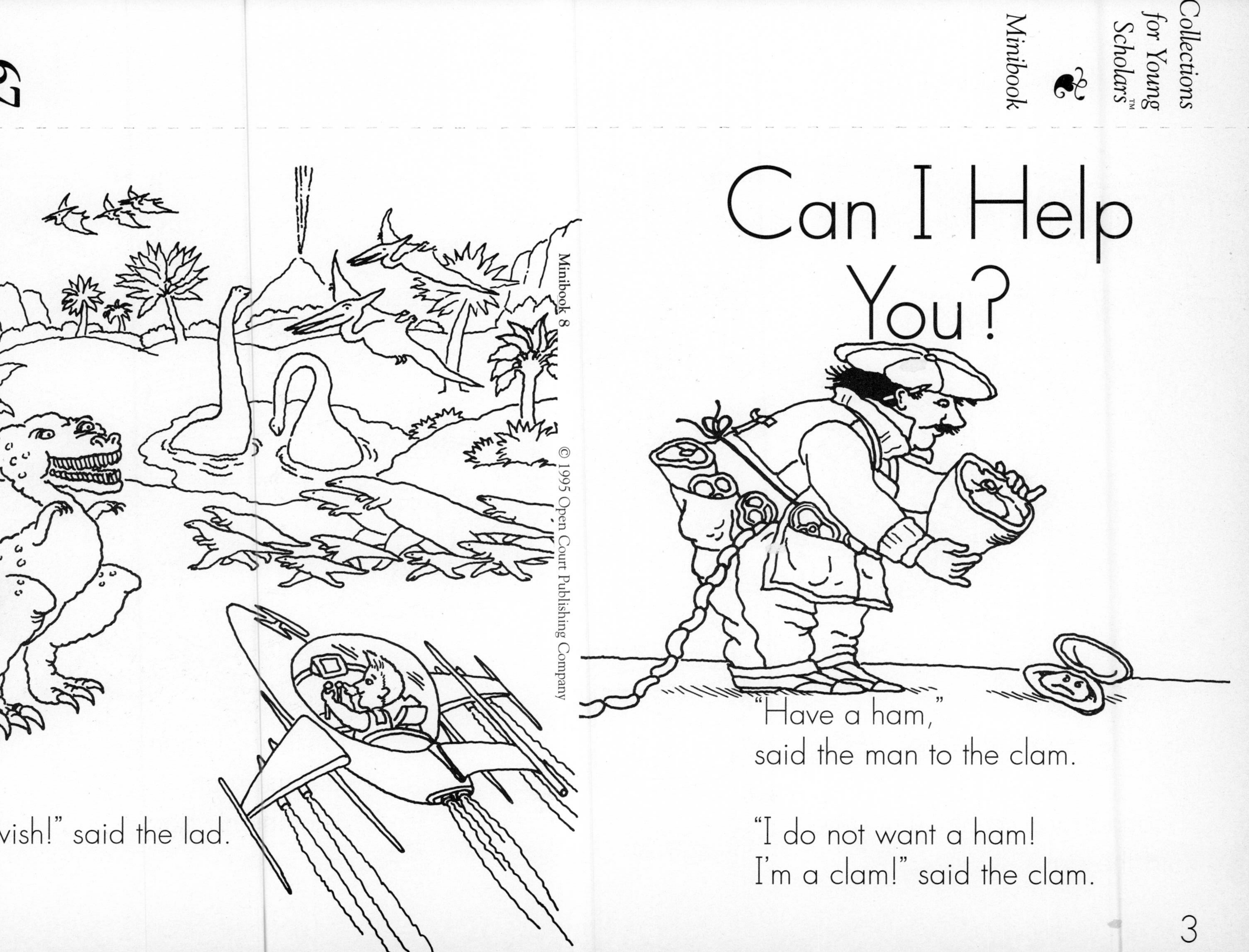

"I wish!" said the lad.

Minibook 8

Can I Help You?

"Have a ham,"
said the man to the clam.

"I do not want a ham!
I'm a clam!" said the clam.

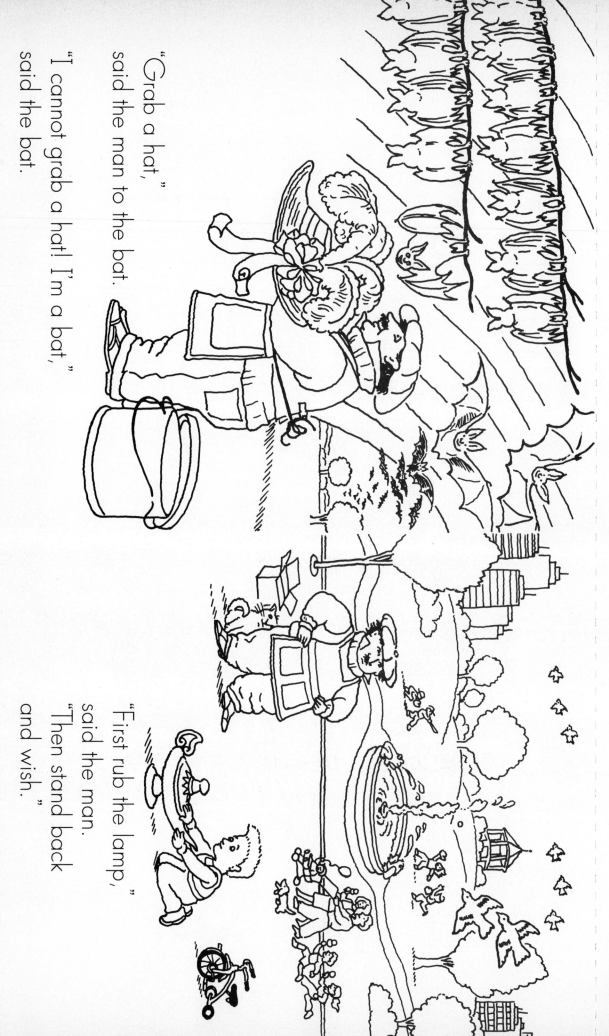

"Grab a hat,"
said the man to the bat.

"I cannot grab a hat! I'm a bat,"
said the bat.

"First rub the lamp,"
said the man.
"Then stand back
and wish."

"It costs a nickel,"
said the man to the lad.

"A nickel!" said the lad.
"What can I do with it?"

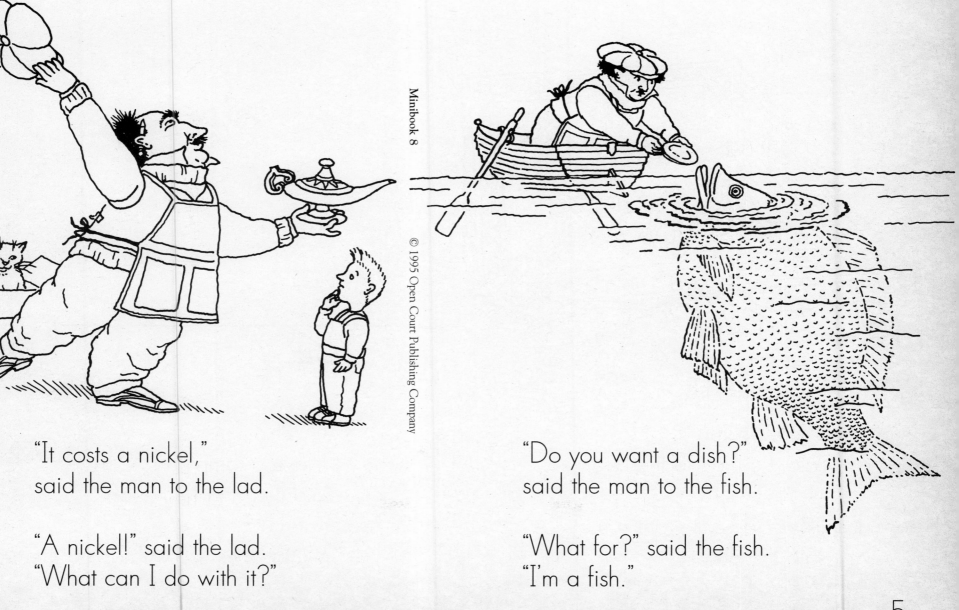

"Do you want a dish?"
said the man to the fish.

"What for?" said the fish.
"I'm a fish."

"Here's a rug,"
said the man to the bug.

"No, I do not want a rug,"
said the bug.

"Have a lamp,"
said the man to the lad.

"What does it cost?" asked the lad.

The Lamp

Minibook 8

"Want a tub?"
said the man to the sub.

"I'm too big for a tub,"
said the sub.

"Have a wig,"
said the man to the pig.

"Not a wig!" said the pig.
"I'm a pig!"

"I can't sell a thing today."

"It's time to dine," said Grace.
"The spider will sit still
until an insect hits the web.
It wants a nice snack."

"Me too!" said Mike. "It's time for lunch!"

The Spider Club

by Alice Cary

illustrated by Diane Blasius

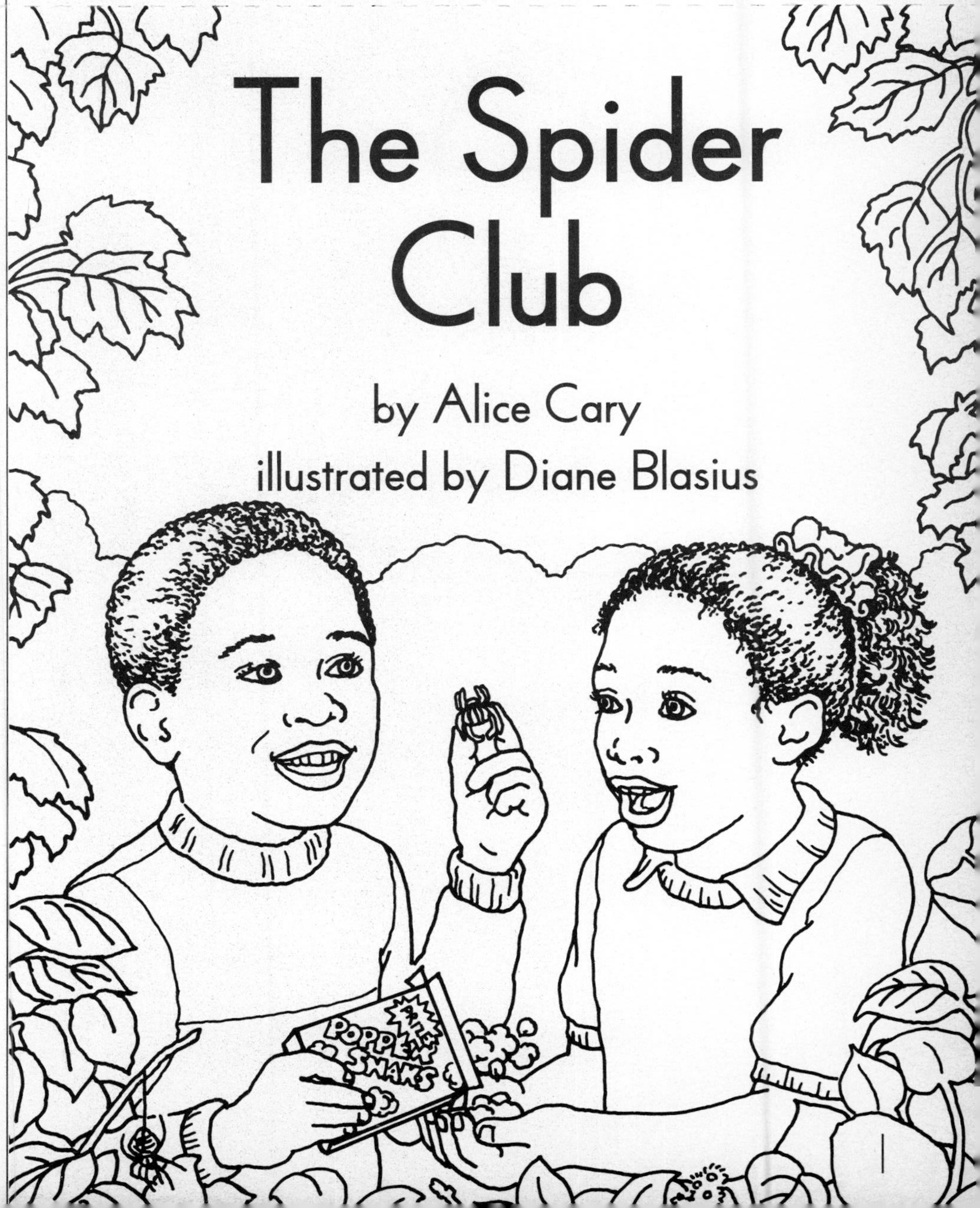

"Next, it fills in the frame," said Grace. "It spins fast."

"What a wonderful web!" said Mike. "What will it do next?"

"What next?" asked Mike.

"The spider runs from bridge to bridge," said Grace.
"It spins and spins to make a frame for the web."

Minibook 9

"Run, Grace!" yelled Mike. "It's a spider!"

"Run?" said Grace. "What for?"

"Girls hate spiders," said Mike.

"Not me," said Grace. "I like spiders. My sister and I have a spider club."

"This silk thread is called a dragline. The spider rides on the end of it. Then the spider makes two bridges."

"What a trick!" said Mike.

"A spider makes two kinds of silk.
One kind sticks to things," said Grace.
"When an insect hits the web,
it sticks to the silk."

"That is a garden spider," said Grace.
"It has eight eyes!"

"It has lots of legs, too," said Mike.

"Yes, all spiders have eight legs,"
said Grace.

"Are all spiders alike?" asked Mike.

Grace led Mike to the Spider Club.
Inside the club were lots of spiders.

"No, not all spiders are alike," Grace said.

"That thread is made of silk," said Grace.

"Isn't silk for shirts?" asked Mike.

"Not spider silk," said Grace.

"Here's a spider!" called Mike. "Will it spin a web?"

"Sit still," said Grace, "and we will find out."

"Oh! It fell from the branch!" yelled Mike. "It made a thread!"

"Here is a spider that jumps," said Grace.

"Jumps? Yikes!" said Mike.

"Not on you," said Grace. "It jumps on insects."

"Can't it spin a web?" asked Mike.

"No," said Grace, "not all spiders spin webs."

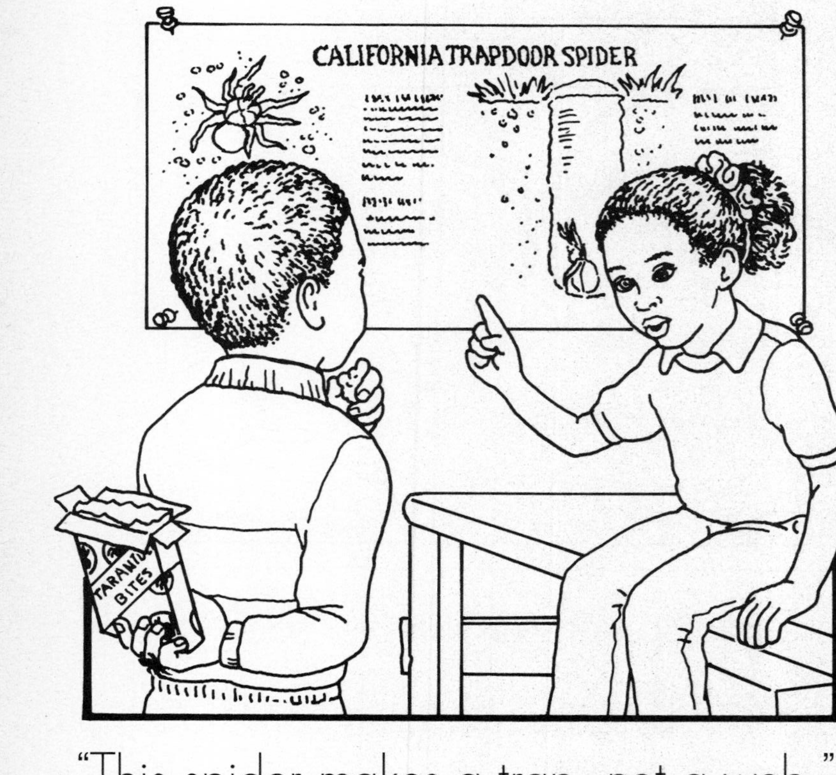

"This spider makes a trap, not a web," said Grace.
"It digs a trap and hides in it.
Insects fall into the trap."

"Which spider do you like best?" asked Mike.

"I like all kinds of spiders," said Grace.
"Crab spiders, pirate spiders, barn spiders,
spiders that fish, and spiders that spit.
But the spiders I like best
are the ones that spin webs.
I bet we can find one outside."

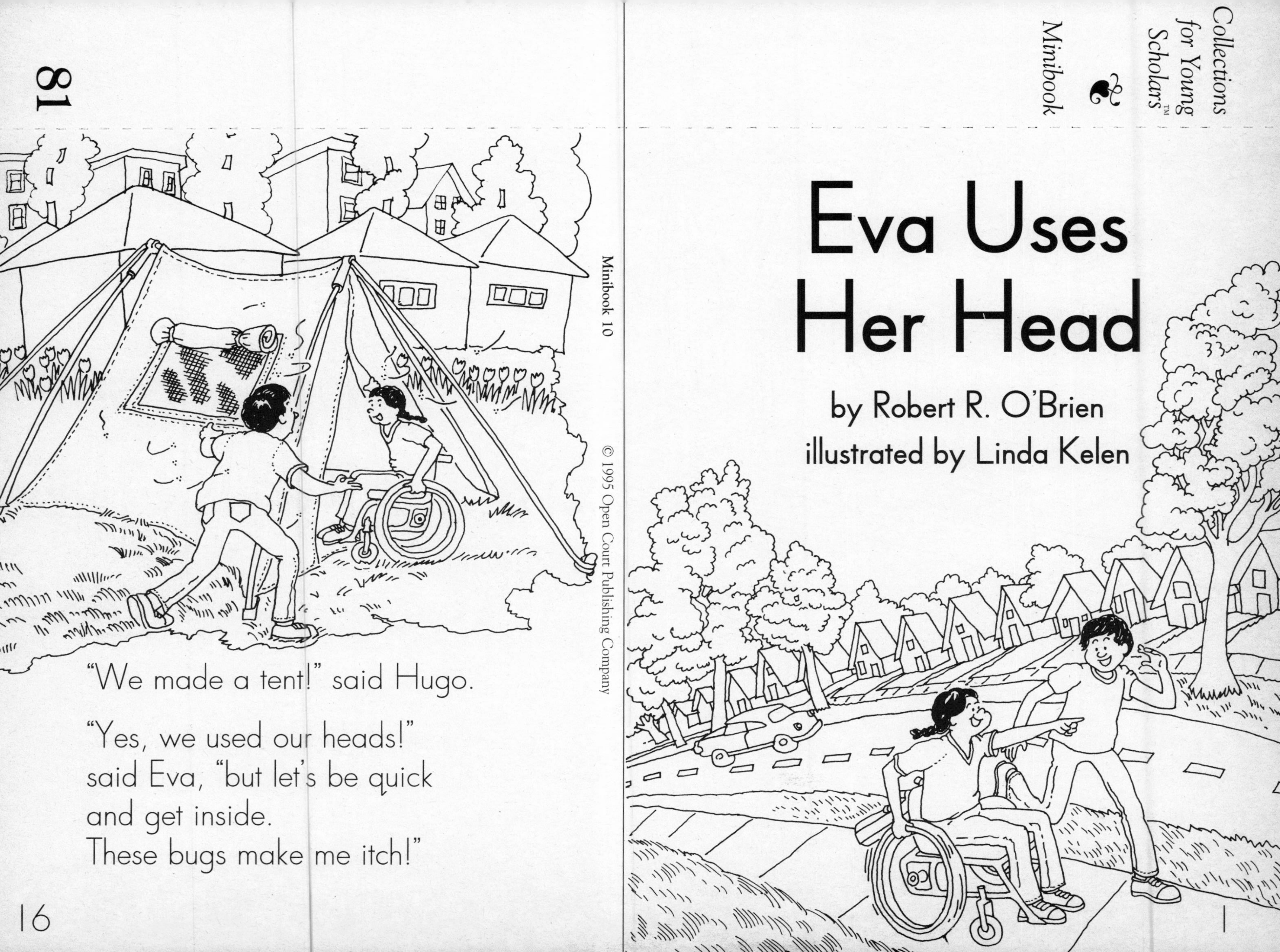

"We made a tent!" said Hugo.

"Yes, we used our heads!"
said Eva, "but let's be quick
and get inside.
These bugs make me itch!"

Minibook 10

Collections for Young Scholars™

Minibook

Eva Uses Her Head

by Robert R. O'Brien
illustrated by Linda Kelen

“I will pull on this end of the rope,” said Eva, “and you pull on that end.”

Eva and Hugo pulled on the rope.

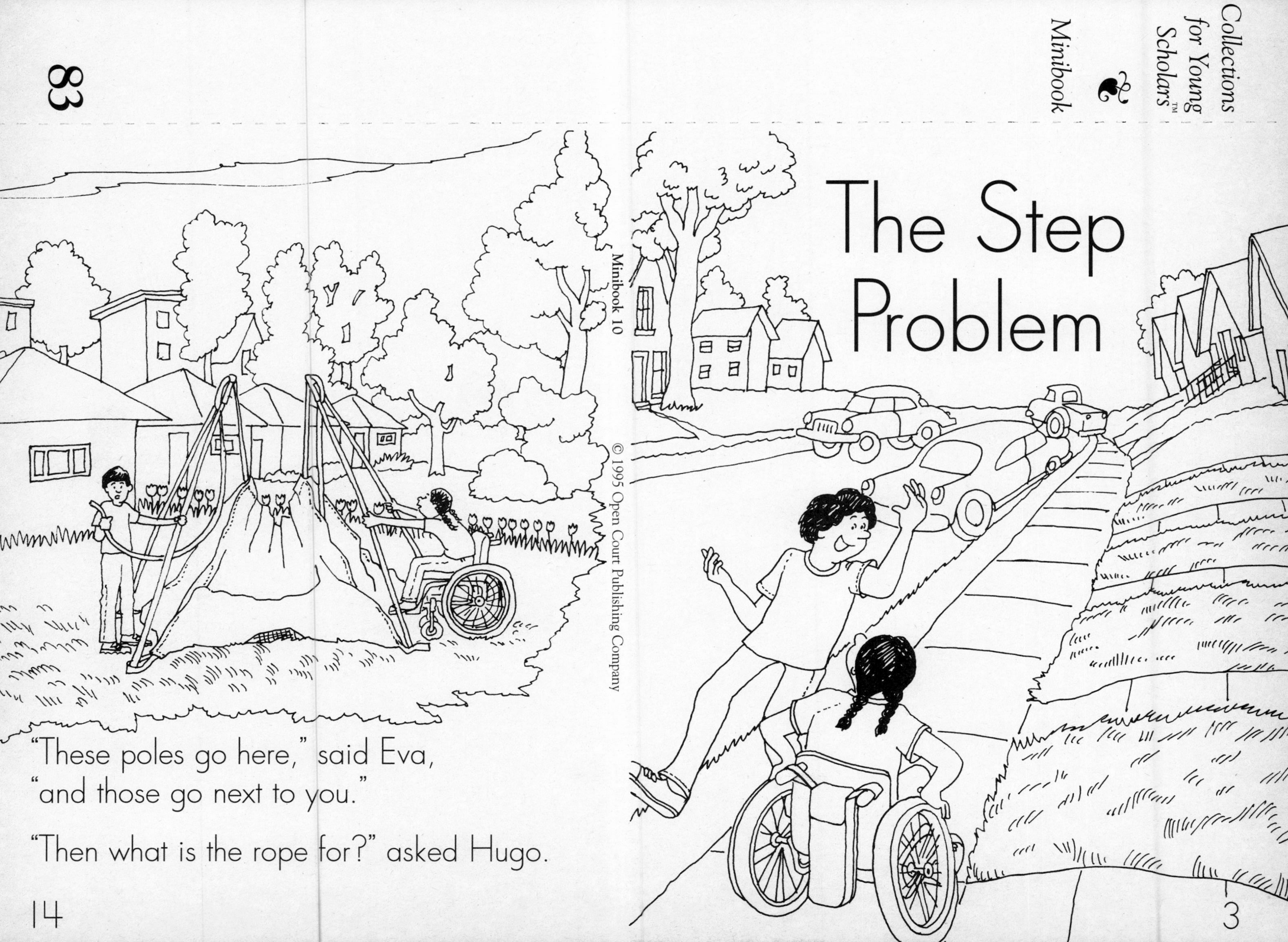

"These poles go here," said Eva, "and those go next to you."

"Then what is the rope for?" asked Hugo.

Minibook 10

The Step Problem

Hugo sat on his front step
and moped.
"Such a sad face, Hugo!" said Nana.
"What has made you so sad?"

"Take these," Eva said.
She held out two poles.

"What are these for?" asked Hugo.

Hugo and Eva sat in Eva's yard.
"Let's go inside," said Hugo.
"These bugs make me itch!"

"I have an idea!" said Eva.

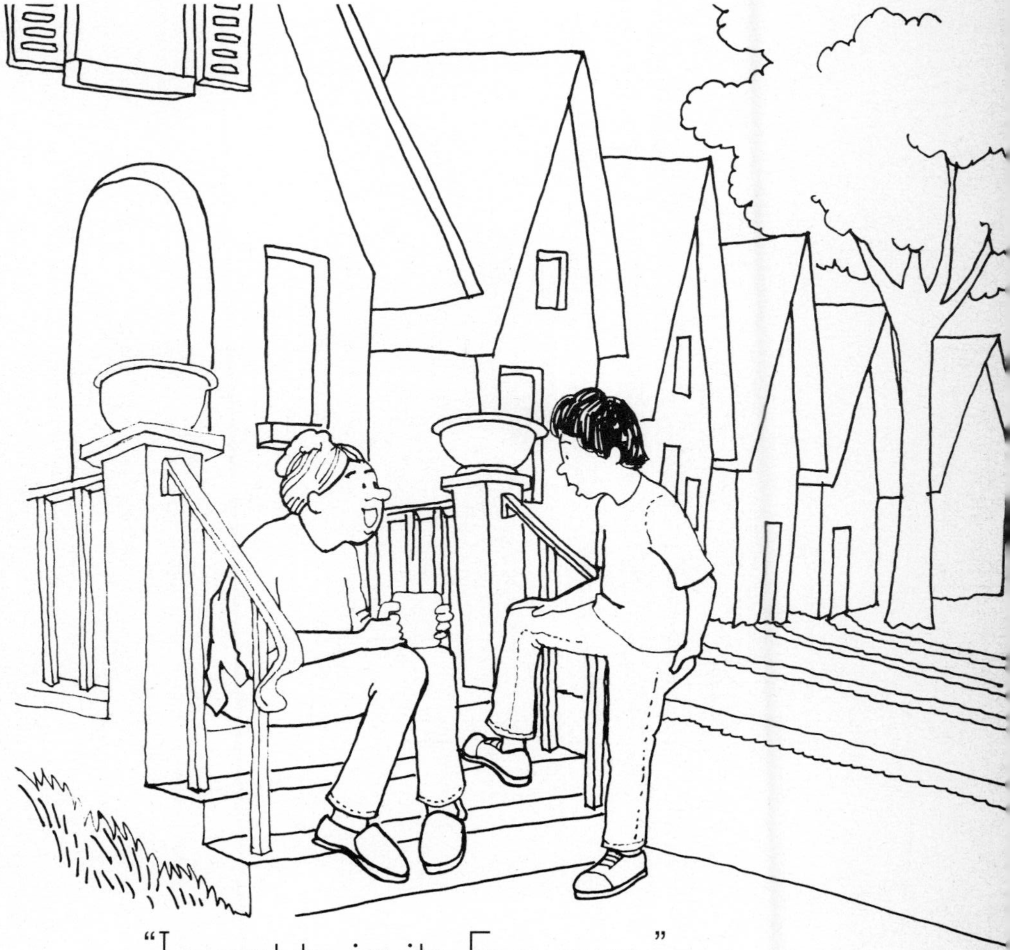

"I want to invite Eva over,"
said Hugo, "but even if she came,
she wouldn't be able
to get up these steps."

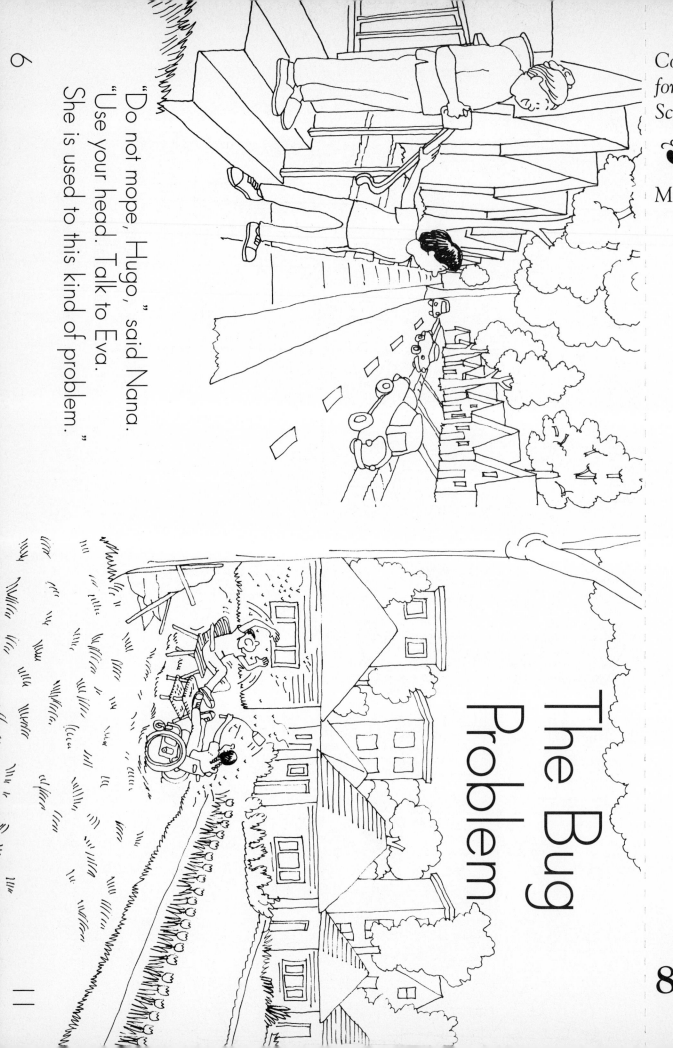

"Do not mope, Hugo," said Nana.
"Use your head. Talk to Eva.
She is used to this kind of problem."

The Bug Problem

Collections for Young Scholars™

Minibook

Hugo talked to Eva.
"No problem!" said Eva.
"Let's go!"

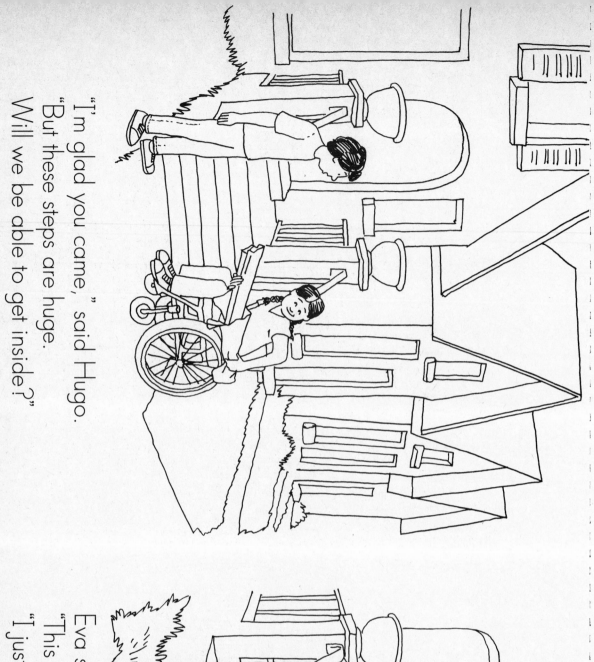

"I'm glad you came," said Hugo.
"But these steps are huge.
Will we be able to get inside?"

Eva smiled.
"This is not a hard problem," she said.
"I just use my head!"

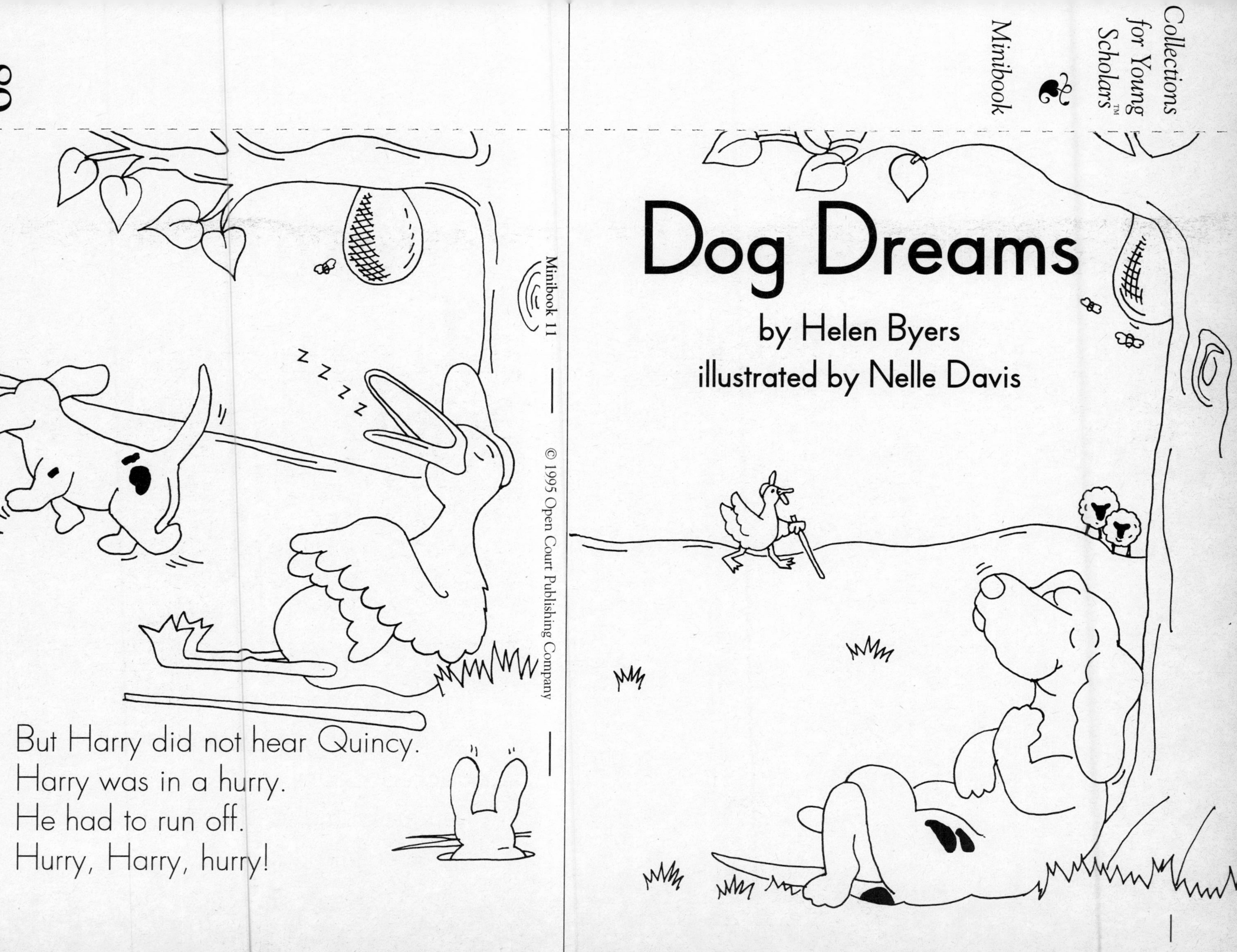

But Harry did not hear Quincy.
Harry was in a hurry.
He had to run off.
Hurry, Harry, hurry!

Minibook 11

Dog Dreams

by Helen Byers
illustrated by Nelle Davis

"You hurry too much, Harry.
You even hurry in your sleep,"
quacked Quincy.
"You make me feel tired.
I need a little nap."

“In the last dream, a fire trapped
three sheep. I had to hurry.
Hurry, Harry, hurry!
I had to lead the sheep
away from the fire!”

14

Minibook 11

Quincy the duck was out for some sun.

3

Collections for Young Scholars™

Minibook

"Quack, quack, quack,"
Quincy said as he went.
"Quack, quack, quack, quack."

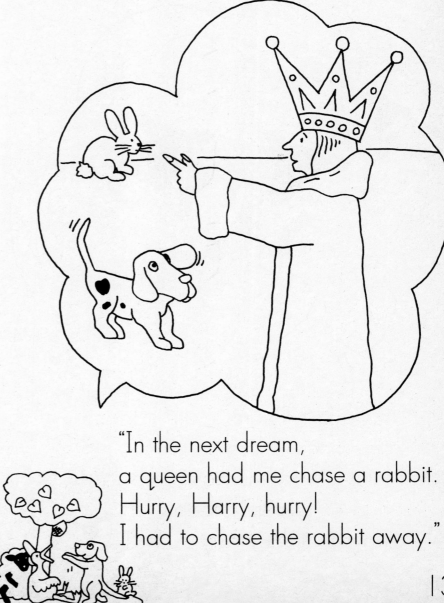

"In the next dream,
a queen had me chase a rabbit.
Hurry, Harry, hurry!
I had to chase the rabbit away."

"In one dream, fleas and bees
were after me. I had to hurry.
Hurry, Harry, hurry!"

Quincy came to a tree
with big green leaves.
A dog was asleep under the tree.

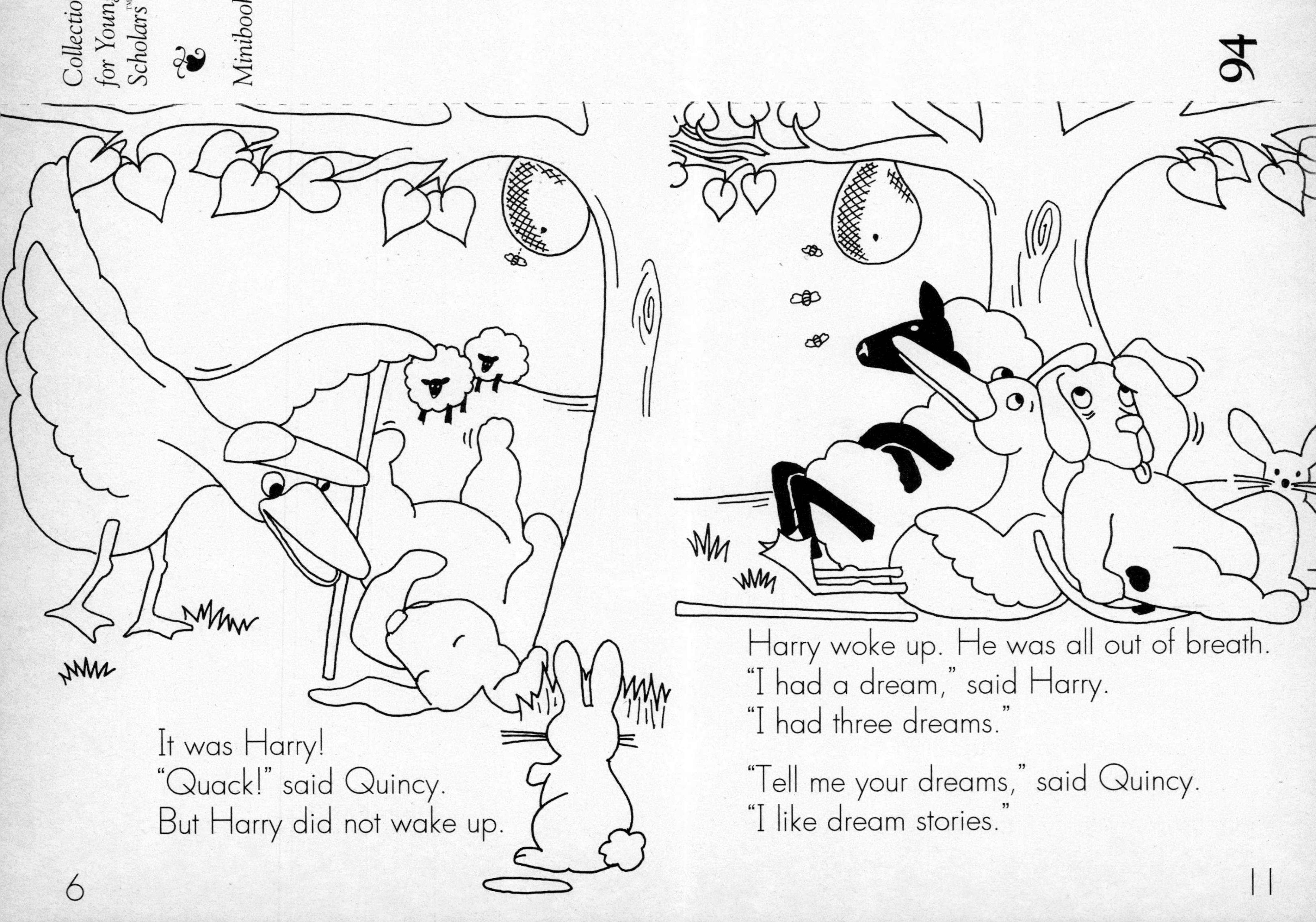

It was Harry!
"Quack!" said Quincy.
But Harry did not wake up.

Harry woke up. He was all out of breath.
"I had a dream," said Harry.
"I had three dreams."

"Tell me your dreams," said Quincy.
"I like dream stories."

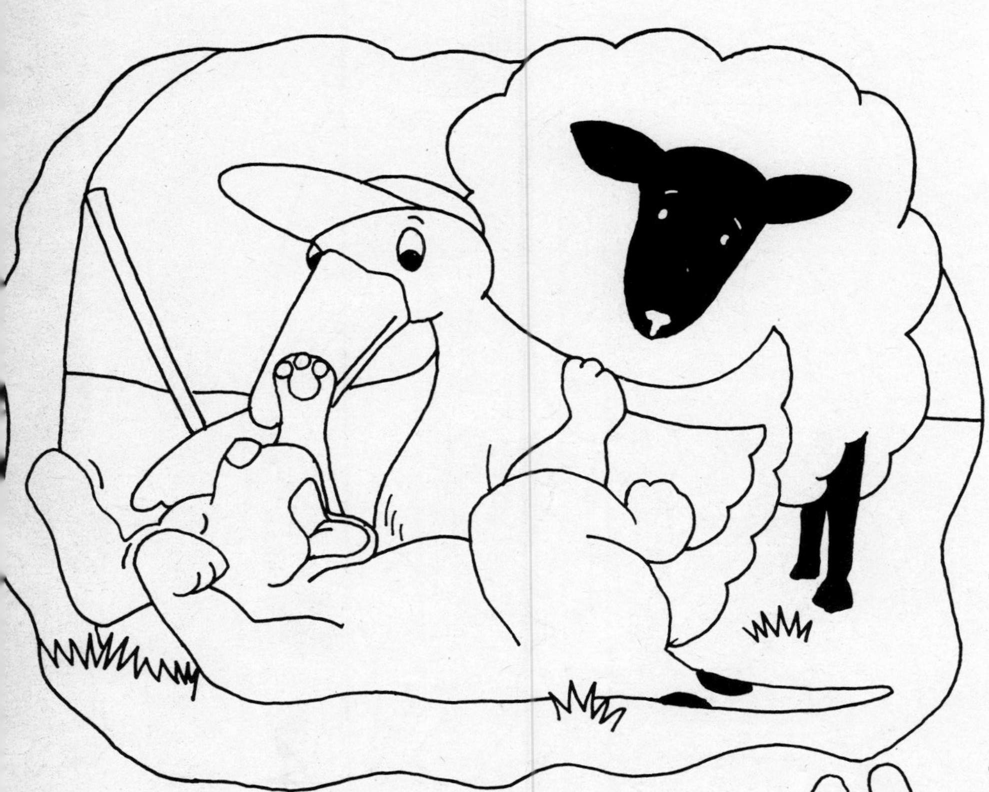

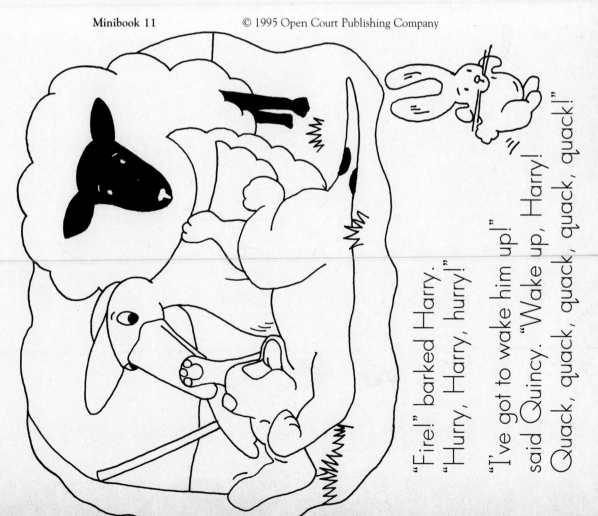

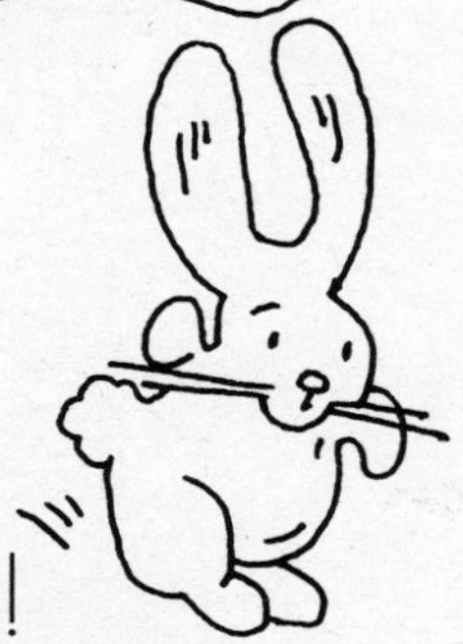

"Fire!" barked Harry.
"Hurry, Harry, hurry!"

"I've got to wake him up!"
said Quincy. "Wake up, Harry!
Quack, quack, quack, quack, quack!"

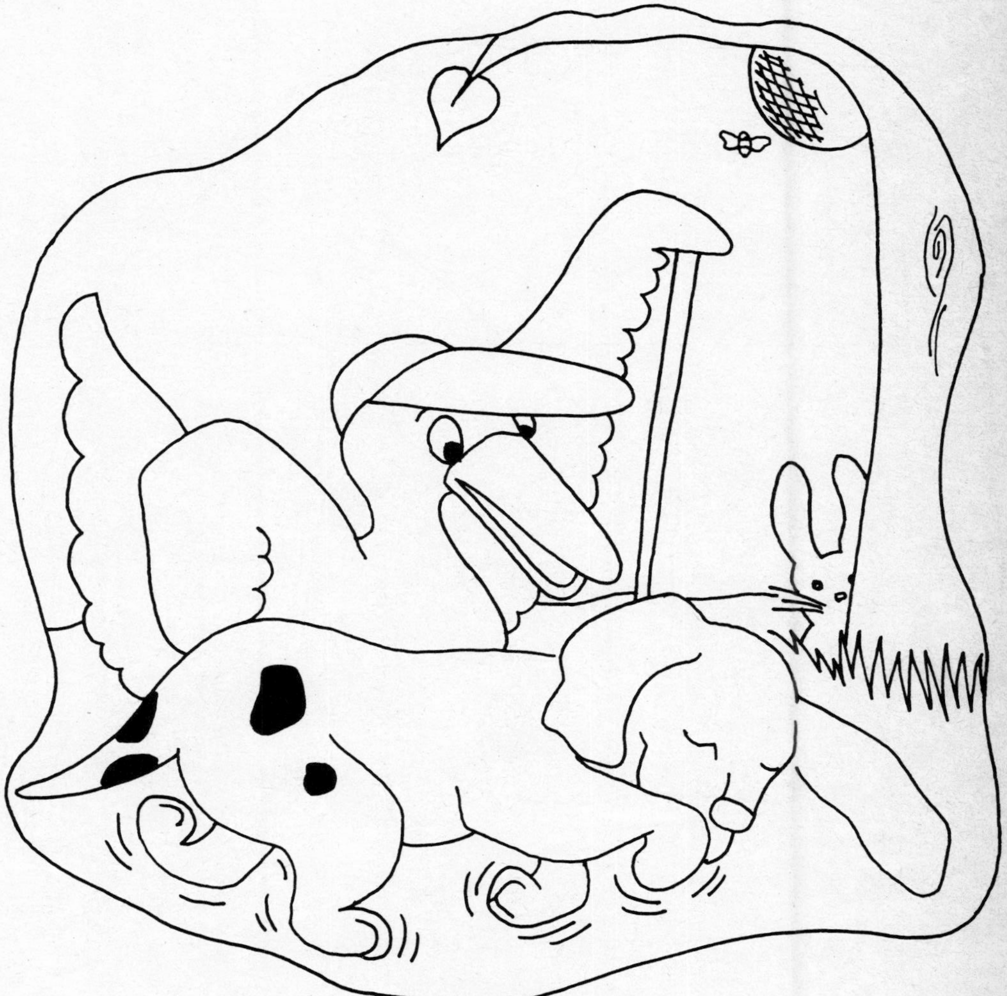

Harry was deep in a dream.
Harry's feet ran in his sleep.

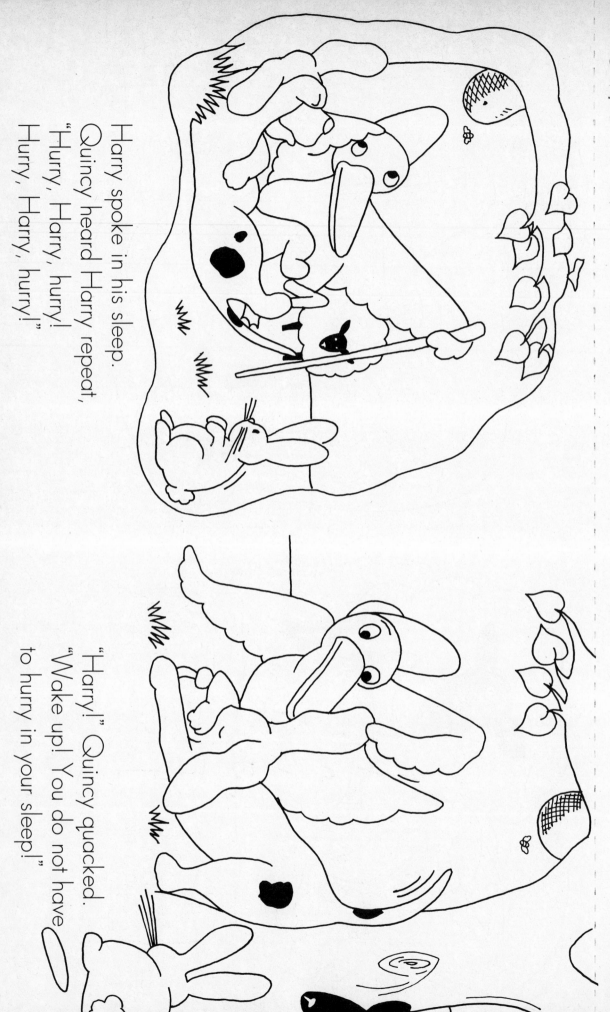

Harry spoke in his sleep.
Quincy heard Harry repeat,
"Hurry, Harry, hurry!
Hurry, Harry, hurry!"

"Harry!" Quincy quacked.
"Wake up! You do not have
to hurry in your sleep!"

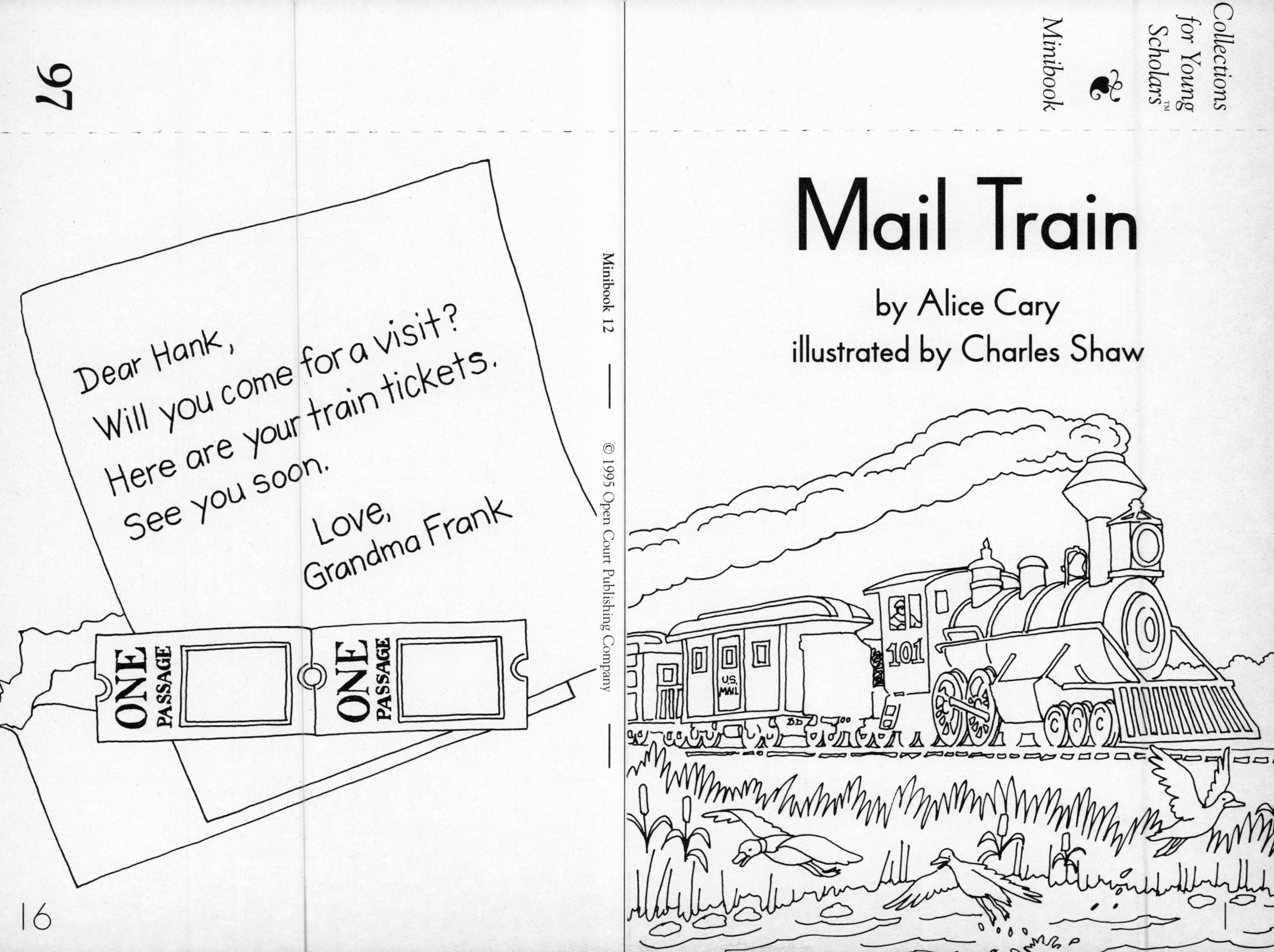
Dear Hank,
Will you come for a visit?
Here are your train tickets.
See you soon.
Love,
Grandma Frank
ONE PASSAGE
ONE PASSAGE
U.S. MAIL
101

Collections for Young Scholars™

Minibook

Mail Train

by Alice Cary

illustrated by Charles Shaw

car-whacker — someone who checks trains

This is the mail carrier
delivering the letter
that Mrs. Frank
sent to her grandson Hank.

This is the platform
where the mail clerk
tosses the bag
that holds the letter
that Mrs. Frank
sent to her grandson Hank.

hotbox — a wheel part
that gets too hot

This is Mrs. Frank
sending a letter
to her grandson Hank.

U.S. MAIL
U.S. MAIL
This is a car-whacker
fixing the mail car
on the train
that carries the bag
that holds the letter
that Mrs. Frank
sent to her grandson Hank.
12
Minibook 12
© 1995 Open Court Publishing Company
U.S. MAIL
This is the bag
that holds the letter
that Mrs. Frank
sent to her grandson Hank.
5

Collections for Young Scholars™

Minibook

This is the train
that carries the bag
that holds the letter
that Mrs. Frank
sent to her grandson Hank.

"Stop the train!"
cries the car-whacker.
"We've got a hotbox!"

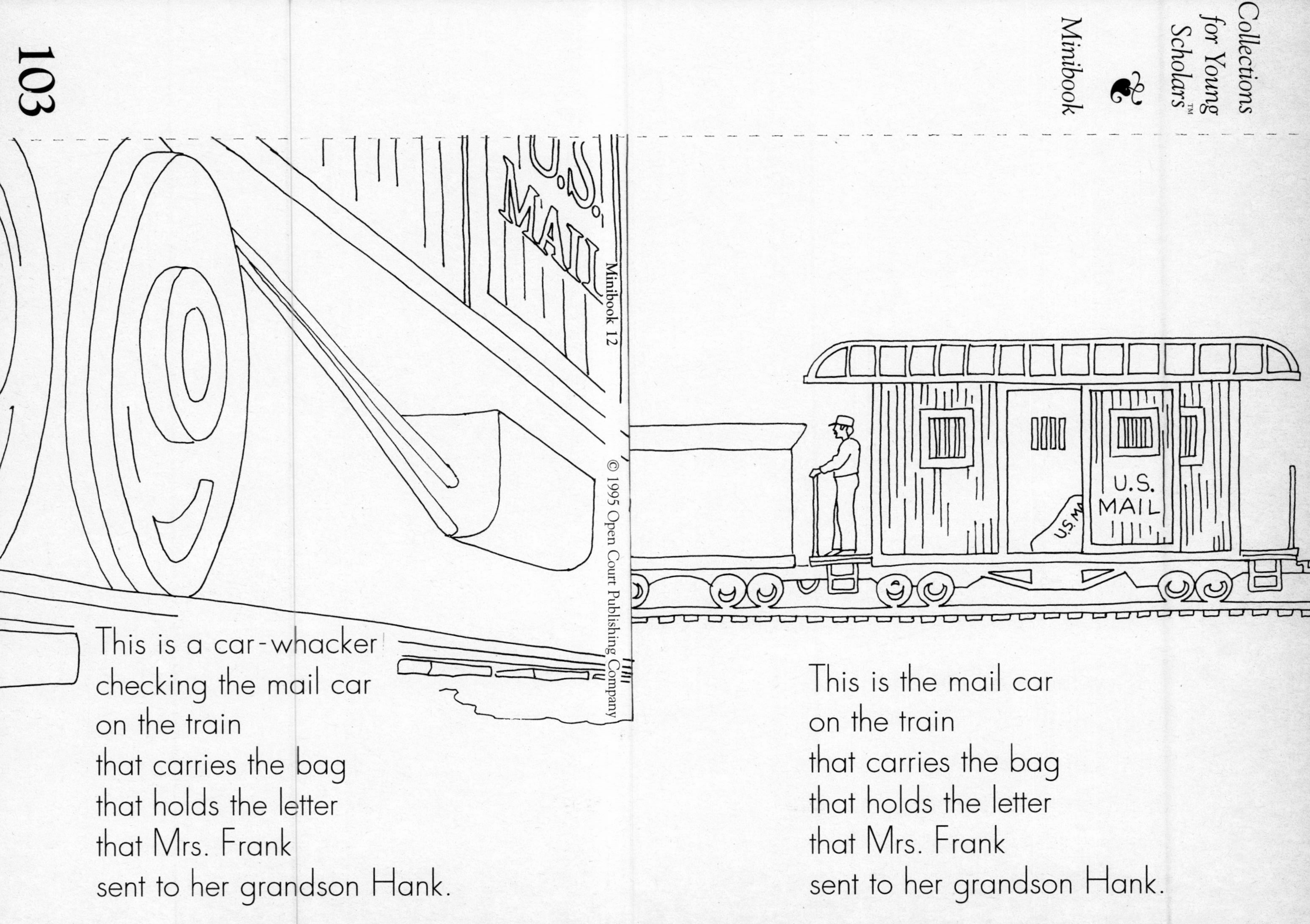

This is a car-whacker
checking the mail car
on the train
that carries the bag
that holds the letter
that Mrs. Frank
sent to her grandson Hank.

This is the mail car
on the train
that carries the bag
that holds the letter
that Mrs. Frank
sent to her grandson Hank.

This is the mail clerk
in the mail car
on the train
that carries the bag
that holds the letter
that Mrs. Frank
sent to her grandson Hank.

U.S. MA

Collections for Young Scholars™

Minibook

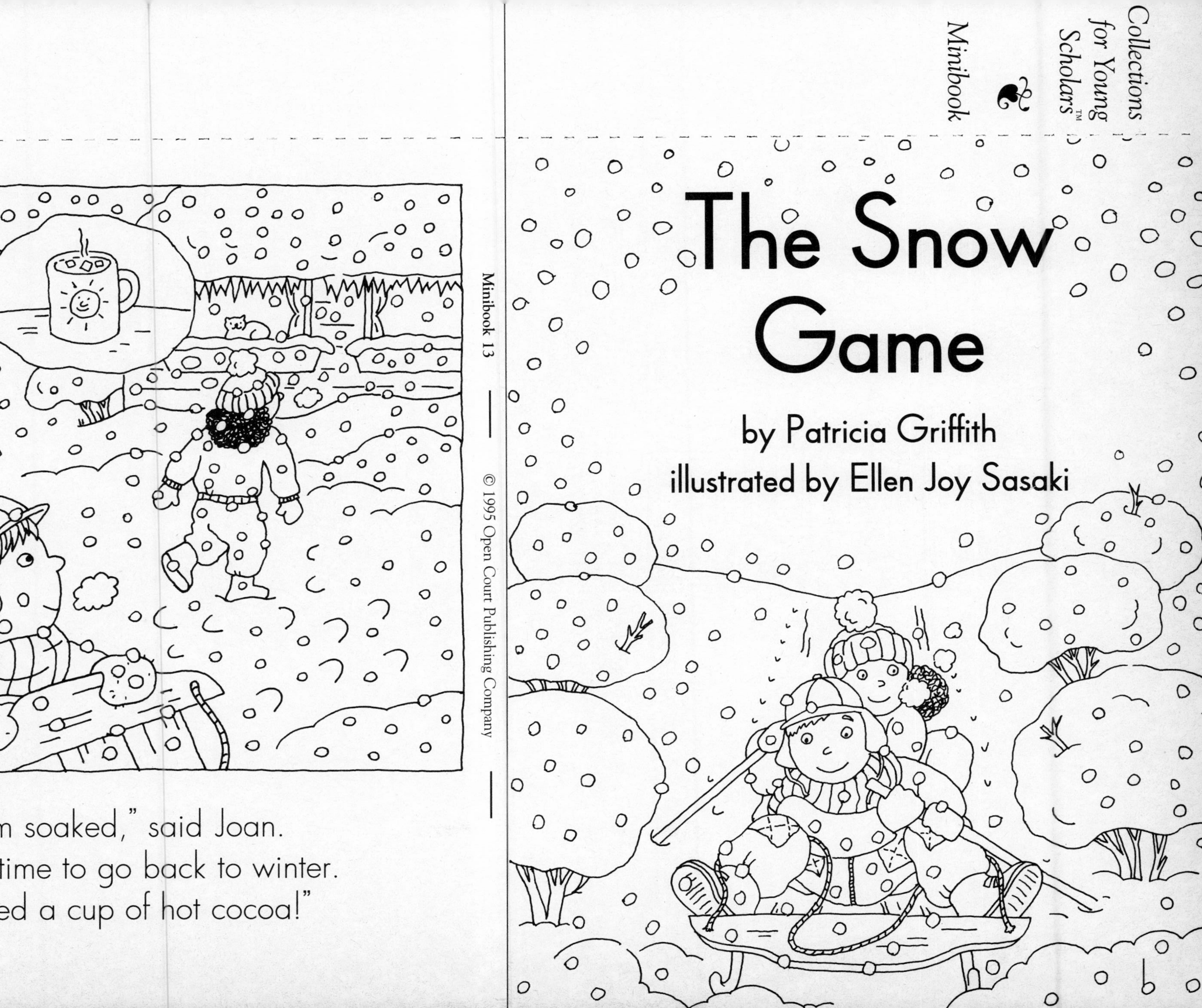

"I am soaked," said Joan.
"It's time to go back to winter.
I need a cup of hot cocoa!"

Minibook 13

The Snow Game

by Patricia Griffith

illustrated by Ellen Joy Sasaki

Collections for Young Scholars™

Minibook

106

2

15

"Whoa!"

"Oh no," moaned Joe. "More snow!"

"More snow?" groaned Joan.
"No! Not more snow!"

"Come to the window," said Joe.
"Snow is on the sidewalks.
Snow is on the roads.
Snow is everywhere!"

"Okay, then we'll just float.
We'll let the wind blow us.
I'll just push us off," said Joe.

"Blow us? Without a sail?" asked Joan.

"Okay, then follow me.
We will go on a boat!
Here are some oars," said Joe.

"Joe, you can't row in snow!" said Joan.

"I'm tired of winter.
I'm tired of the cold.
And I'm tired of the snow!"
moaned Joan.

"We could make a snowman
or go sledding," said Joe.

"I'm tired of snowmen, and
I'm tired of sledding," said Joan.
"I just want summer to come."

"Here, I'll show you," said Joe.
"Take this pail and some coal."

"It still looks like a snowman,"
said Joan.

"The sand is so hot.
Wiggle your toes in it.
We'll make a sand castle," said Joe.

"A <u>sand</u> castle?" asked Joan.

Minibook 13

"Okay," said Joe. "Then
we will make summer come.
We will go to the beach.
Get your coat. Here we go."

"Here we are at the coast," said Joe.
"Do you like it?"

"This is the coast?" asked Joan.
"It's a yard full of snow!"

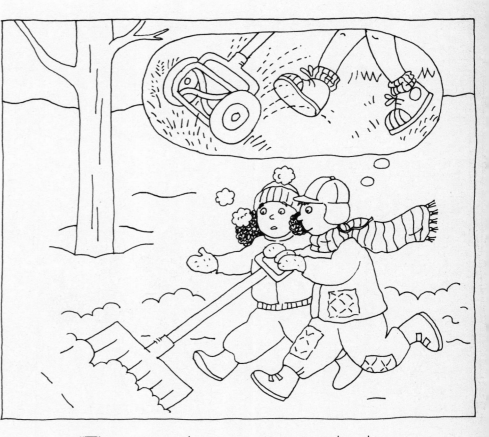

"The grass has grown too high.
We can't see the water.
Help me mow a path," said Joe.

"We are mowing?" asked Joan.

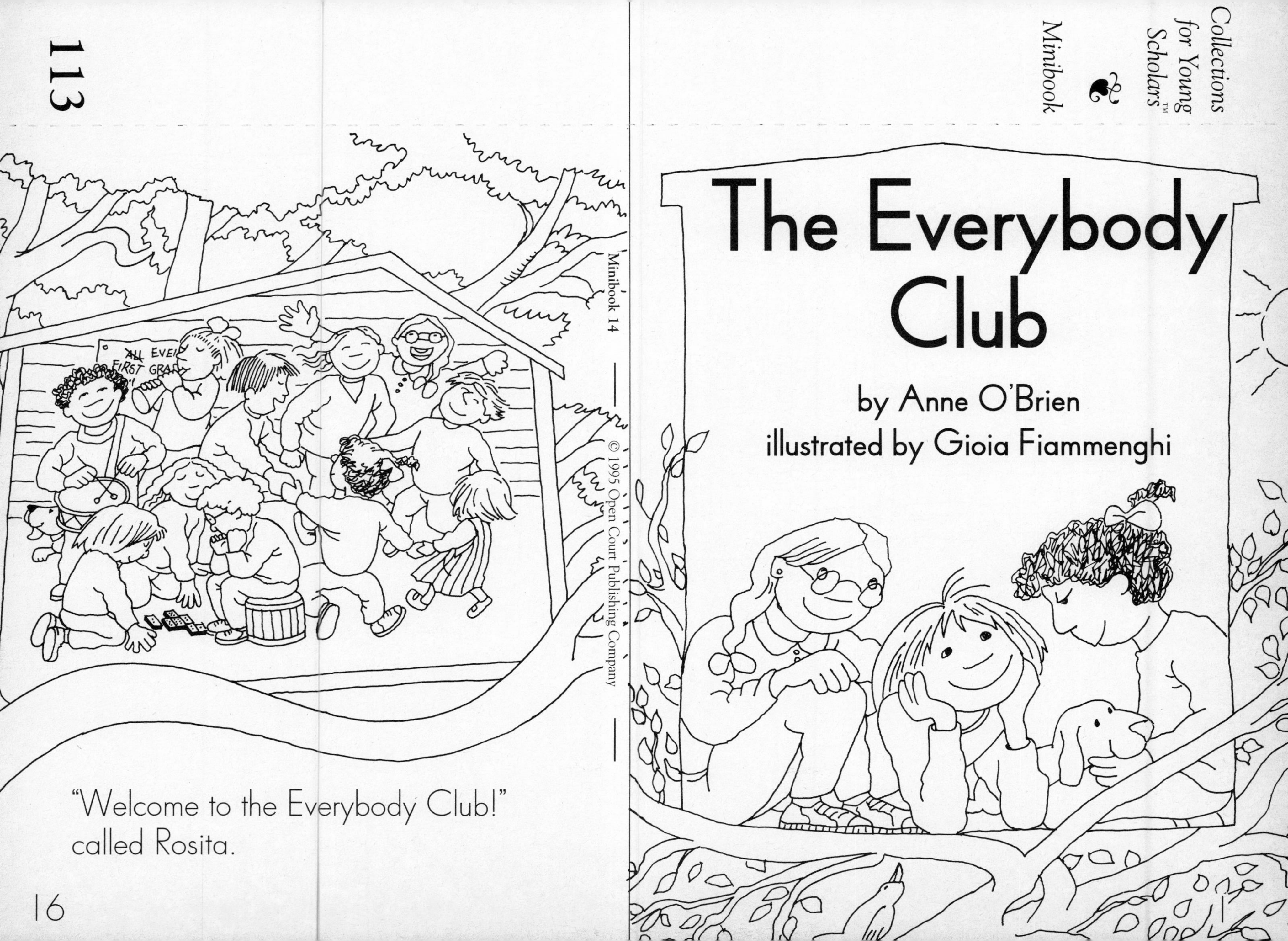

"Welcome to the Everybody Club!"
called Rosita.

Minibook 14

Collections for Young Scholars™

Minibook

The Everybody Club

by Anne O'Brien

illustrated by Gioia Fiammenghi

"It's getting crowded!" said Rosita.
"How about just calling it
the Everybody Club?"

Abby crossed out All Grades
and painted Everybody.
Then she painted lots of faces.

"Hi!" called Abby's little sister.
"Can I come up?"

"Well," said Abby, "we have a club.
It's called the All Grades Club,
and you aren't even in kindergarten!"

Minibook 14

Abby and Rosita went over
to Quanda's yard to play.

"Come on!" called Quanda.
"We can play in the tree house!"

"Well," said Quanda,
"how about the All Grades Club?"

Abby crossed out First,
added an s, and painted All.
Then she painted another face.

"Now we are the All Grades Club!" said Rosita.

"Hi!" called Quanda's big brother.
"Can I come up?"

"Well," said Quanda, "we have a club.
It's called the First Grade Club,
and you aren't in first grade."

Quanda's big brother scowled.

"Wow! What a neat place!" said Abby.

"Let's make a club!" said Rosita.
"We can call it the Three Girls Club."

Quanda got out paints and paper.
Abby painted Three Girls Club
and three faces on the paper.

"Well," said Quanda,
"how about the First Grade Club?"

Abby crossed out Girls
and painted First Grade.
Then she painted another face.

"Now we are the First Grade Club!" said Rosita.

"Hi!" called David. "Can I come up?"

"Well," said Quanda, "we have a club.
It's called the Girls Club,
and you aren't a girl."

David frowned. He kicked the dirt.

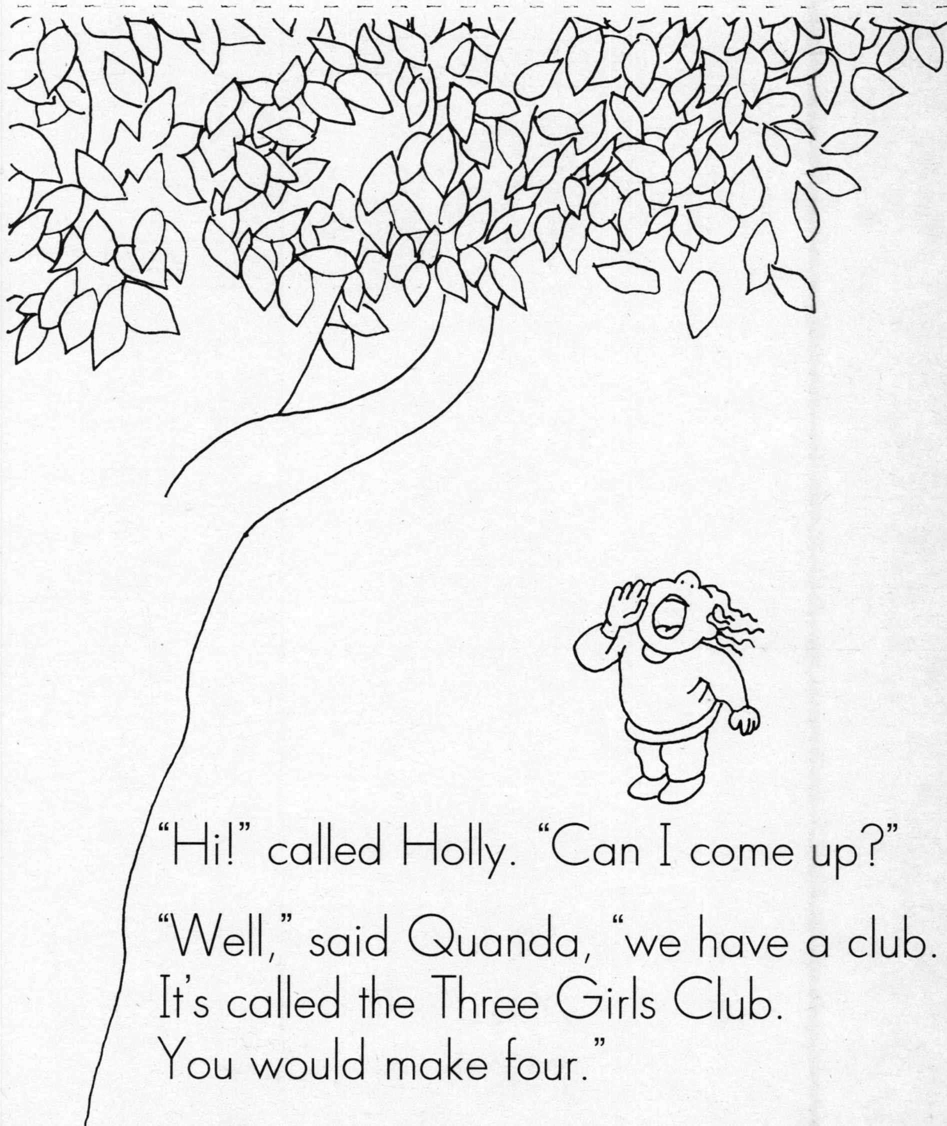

"Hi!" called Holly. "Can I come up?"

"Well," said Quanda, "we have a club.
It's called the Three Girls Club.
You would make four."

Holly looked down. She hung her head.

"Well," said Quanda,
"how about just the Girls Club?"

Abby crossed out Three
and painted another face.

"Now we are the Girls Club!" said Rosita.

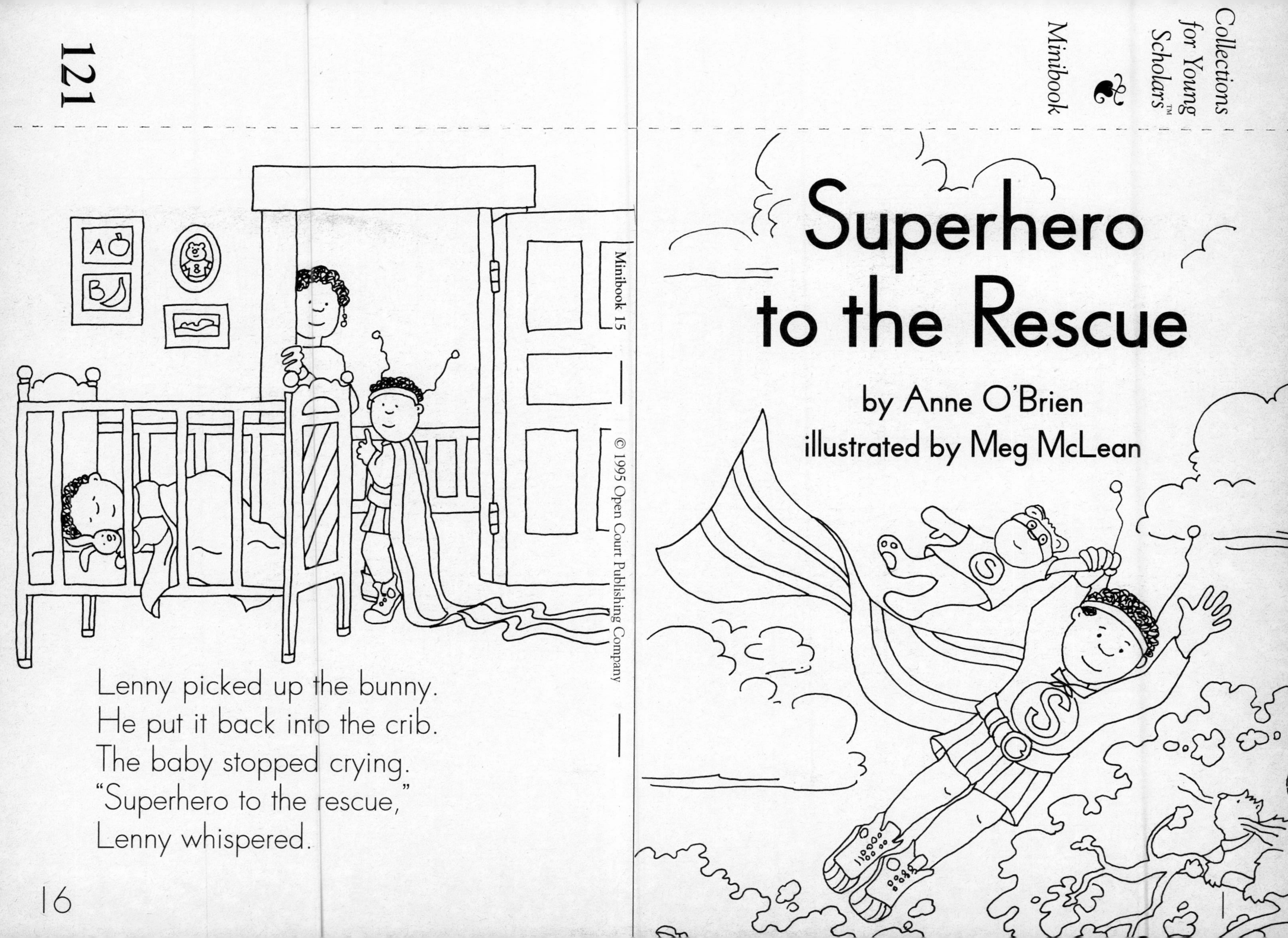

Lenny picked up the bunny.
He put it back into the crib.
The baby stopped crying.
"Superhero to the rescue,"
Lenny whispered.

Minibook 15

Collections for Young Scholars™

Minibook

Superhero to the Rescue

by Anne O'Brien

illustrated by Meg McLean

Lenny went upstairs.
The baby was crying.
His bunny had fallen out of the crib.

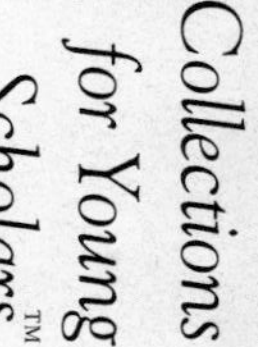

At naptime Lenny was bored.
His mom had put Nikki
and the baby to bed.

Minibook 15

Lenny wanted to be a superhero.

Lenny put on his cape.
"Superhero to the rescue!"
he shouted.
He raced downstairs.

Lenny's mom found him in the tree.
She helped him get down.
"Play something safer," she said.
They went back inside.

"Superhero to the rescue!"
shouted Lenny.
He reached for a branch.

Minibook 15

Lenny landed on top
of his little sister Nikki.
"Ouch!" shouted Nikki.
She began to cry.

"Play something quiet,"
said Lenny's mom.

"Pow! Wow!" shouted Lenny.
He raced to the oak tree.
Lenny's cat sat on one branch.
"Meow!" cried the cat.

"Play something quieter,"
said Lenny's mom.
Lenny went outside.

Lenny and Nikki played house
with the baby.
Nikki grabbed the baby's doll.

"Superhero to the rescue!"
shouted Lenny.
He pushed Nikki out of the way.

Nikki and the baby
both began to cry.

Mr. Lee was an artist.
His glass made rainbows dance in rooms.
It also made him brave.

Minibook 16

Collections for Young Scholars™

Minibook

Mr. Lee

by Jennifer Jacobson
illustrated by John Agee

Mr. Lee turned around.
The chair was not knocking.
The drapes were not swaying.
The tablecloth was not floating.
The hat was not tipping.
It was not dark and scary in there.
Rainbows danced in the room.

Mr. Lee felt a breeze.
He found a broken window.
He put in the new window.
It was a perfect fit.

Minibook 16

Mr. Lee was a timid man.
He was also an artist.
Mr. Lee made stained glass windows.
His glass made rainbows dance in rooms.

One day, Mr. Lee made
a window pane for an inn.
He took the window pane to the inn.
The inn was far away.
Timid Mr. Lee walked and walked.

Timid Mr. Lee walked in.
It was dark and scary.
A chair was knocking,
drapes were swaying,
a tablecloth was floating,
a hat was tipping.

Collections for Young Scholars™

Minibook

Minibook 16

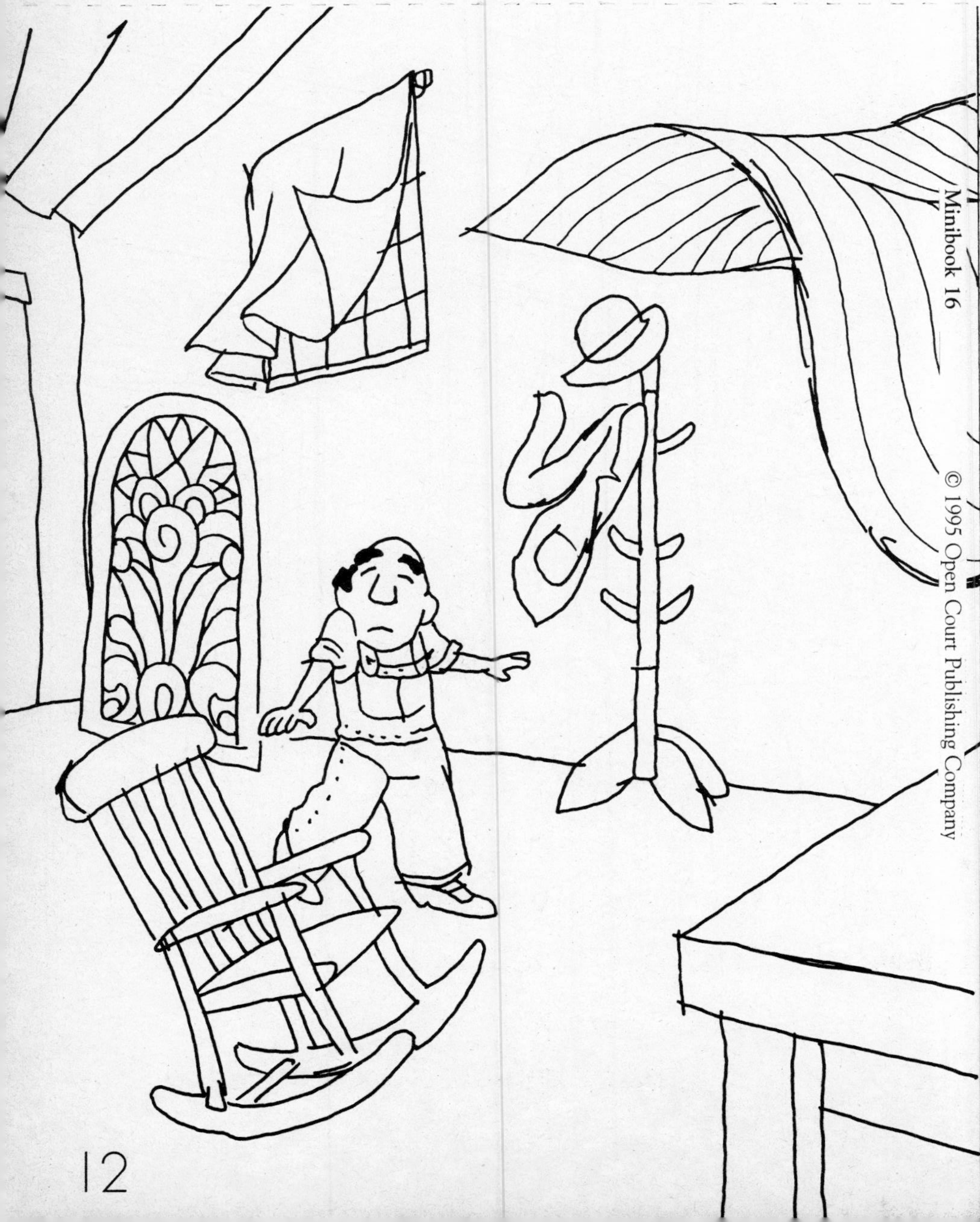

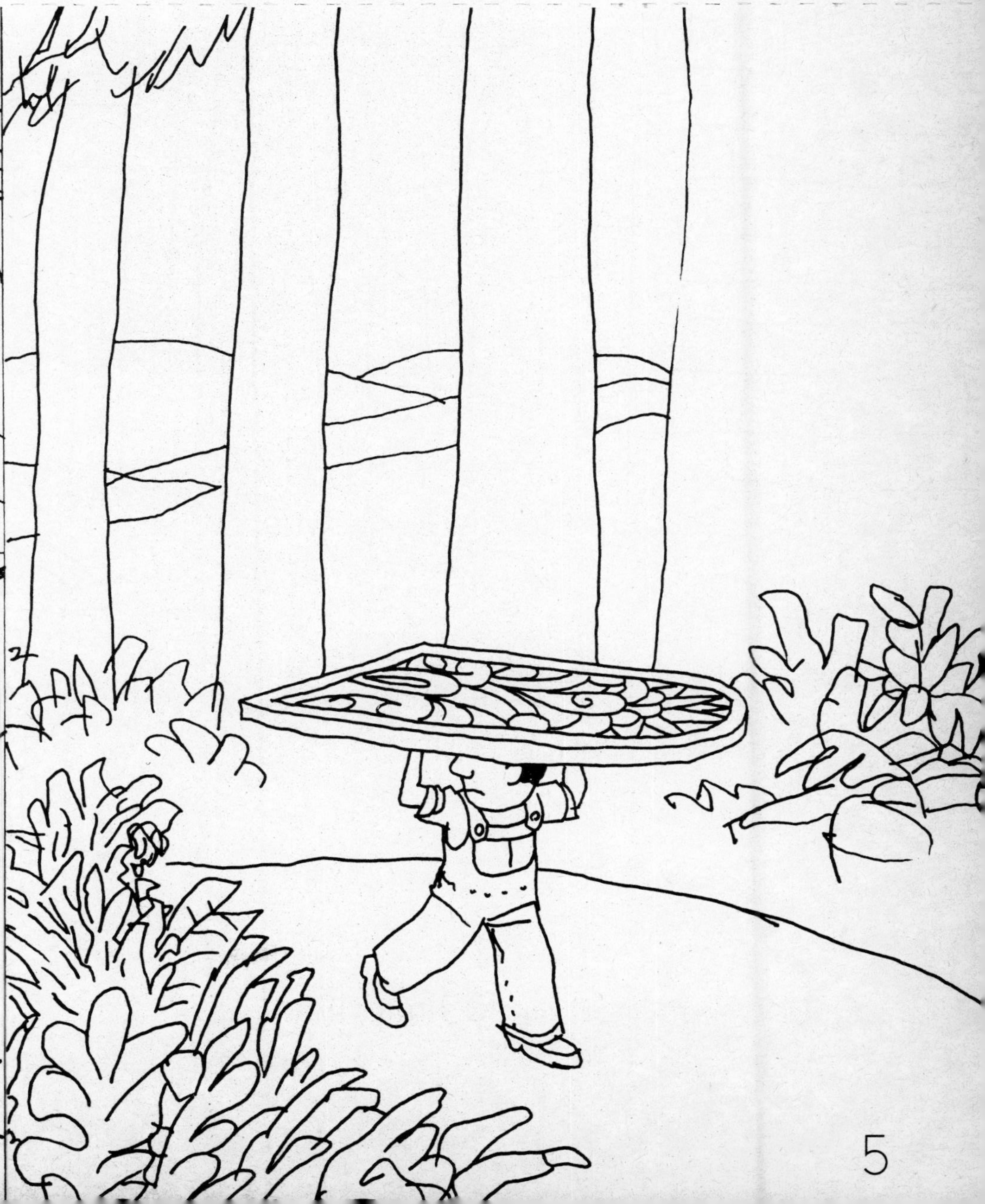

Mr. Lee came to the town where the inn was.
Down the street ran a maid.
"Turn back!" she cried.
"Do not go to the inn!
A chair is knocking.
Drapes are swaying.
It's dark and scary in there!"

"Stay with me," said timid Mr. Lee.
"We will go together."

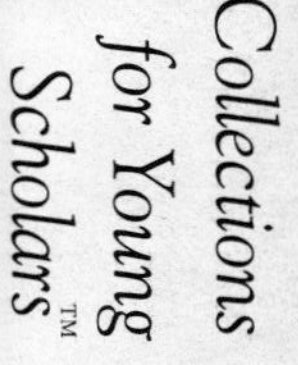

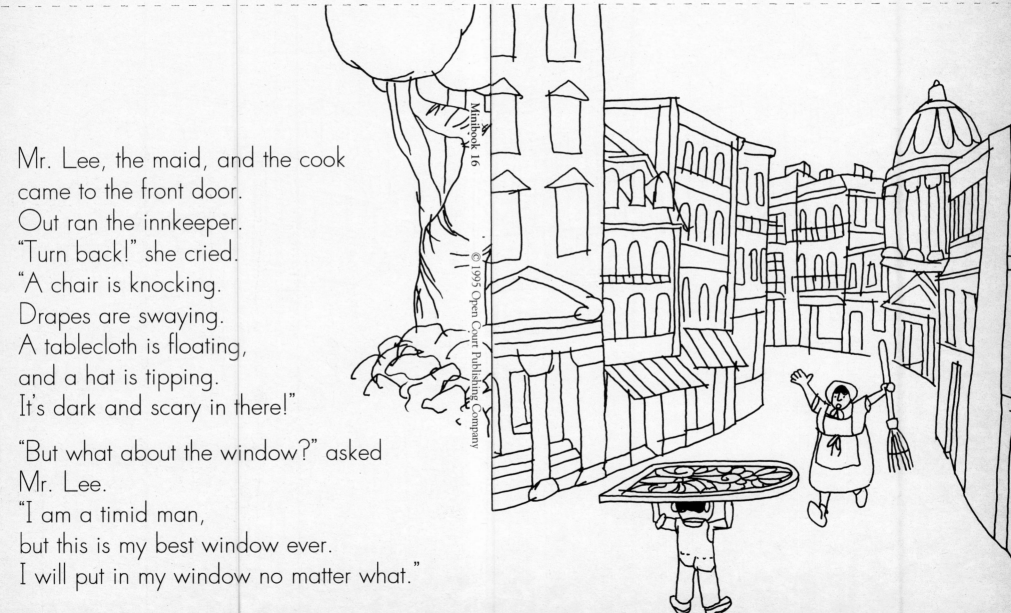

Mr. Lee, the maid, and the cook
came to the front door.
Out ran the innkeeper.
"Turn back!" she cried.
"A chair is knocking.
Drapes are swaying.
A tablecloth is floating,
and a hat is tipping.
It's dark and scary in there!"

"But what about the window?" asked
Mr. Lee.
"I am a timid man,
but this is my best window ever.
I will put in my window no matter what."

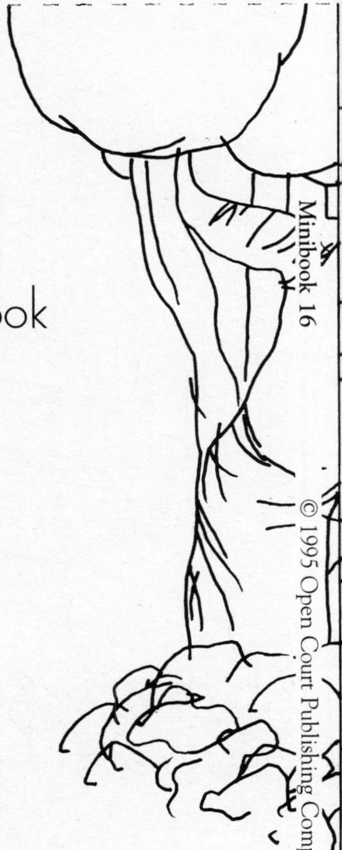

Minibook 16

Mr. Lee and the maid came to a gate.
Out ran a cook waving a spoon.
"Turn back!" cried the cook.
"A chair is knocking.
Drapes are swaying.
A tablecloth is floating.
It's dark and scary in there!"

"Stay with me," said timid Mr. Lee.
"We will go together."

Then the real princess
ordered her royal sister
to take the marbles,
the wrench,
the toy truck,
Cuddles,
and the sneakers,
out from under her royal mattress.

Princess Julia

by Patricia Griffith
illustrated by Pat Doyle

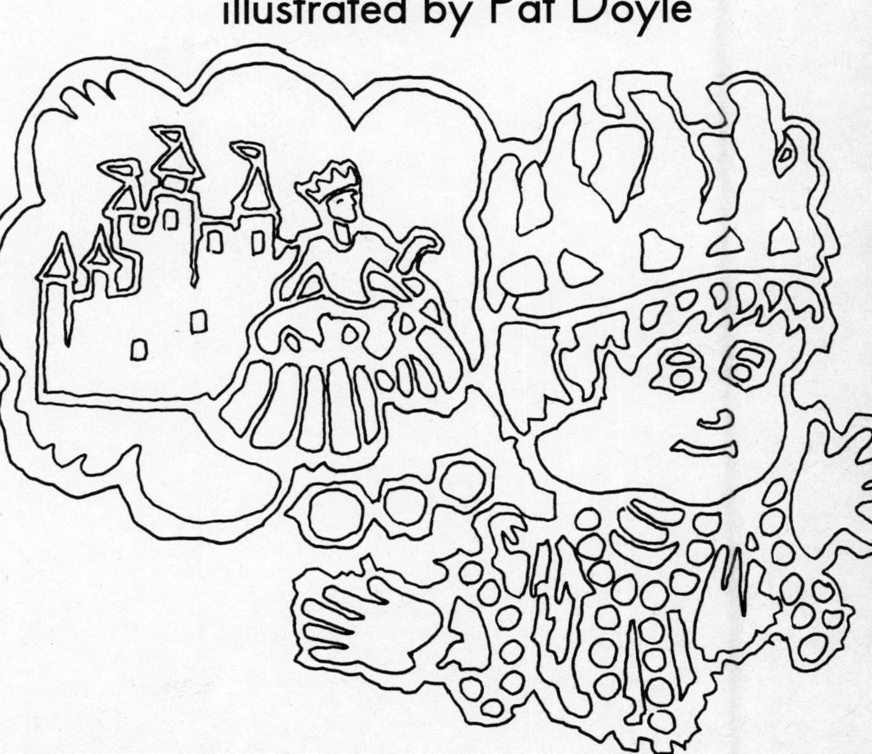

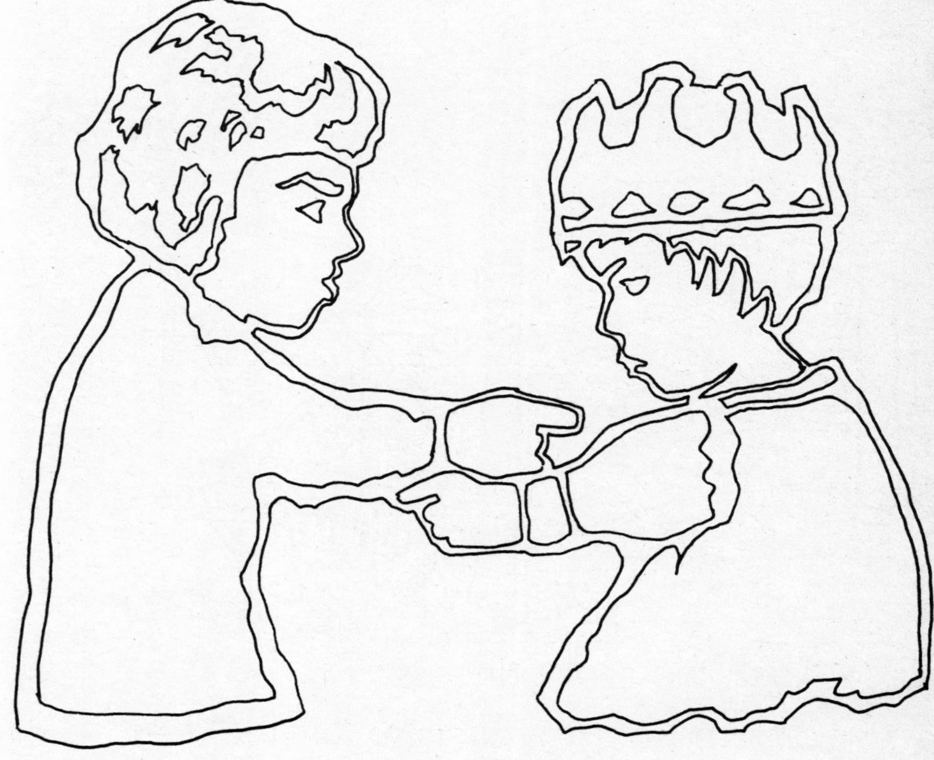

Julia put on her wrinkled crown.
"That was only a fairy tale," she said.
"A real princess can sleep
any place, any time,
any way she wants!
And I am a real princess!"

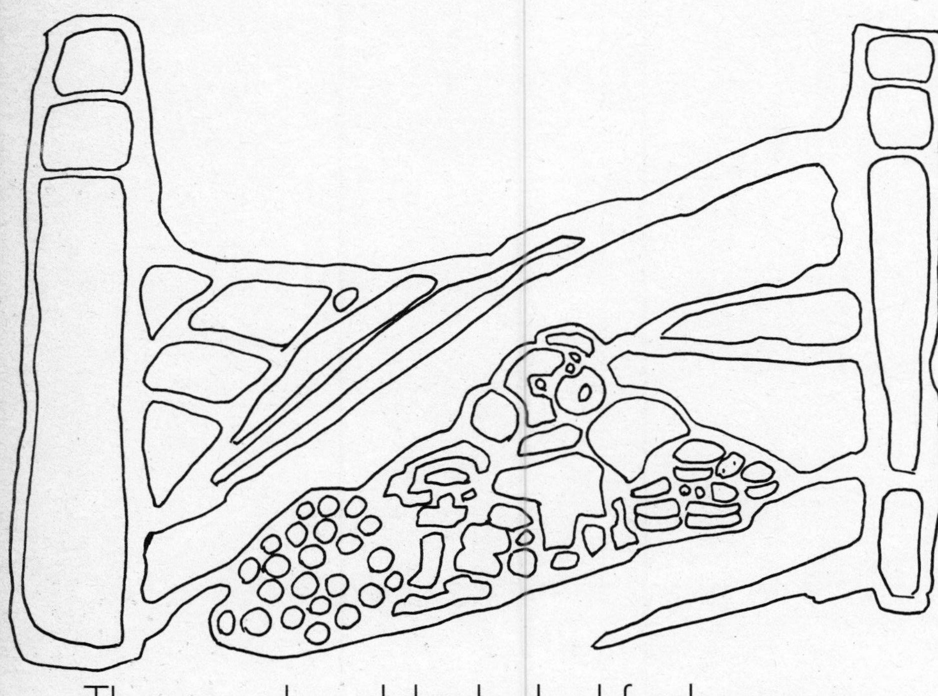

The next day, Julia looked for her crown.
I picked up her mattress.
"You see?" I said.
"You are not a real princess!
Remember <u>The Princess and the Pea</u>?
Look under your bed!
No real princess could sleep on all that!"

Minibook 17 

My little sister Julia thinks
she is a princess.
She thinks she is a real one.

Julia wears fancy gowns and shoes.
She wears a silly paper crown.
She even wears the crown to bed!
"I'm a princess! A real princess!" Julia says.

The night after that, I put
a bag of marbles,
a wrench,
a toy truck,
Cuddles the bear,
my old sneakers,
and Julia's own crown
under her mattress.
Julia never even missed Cuddles!

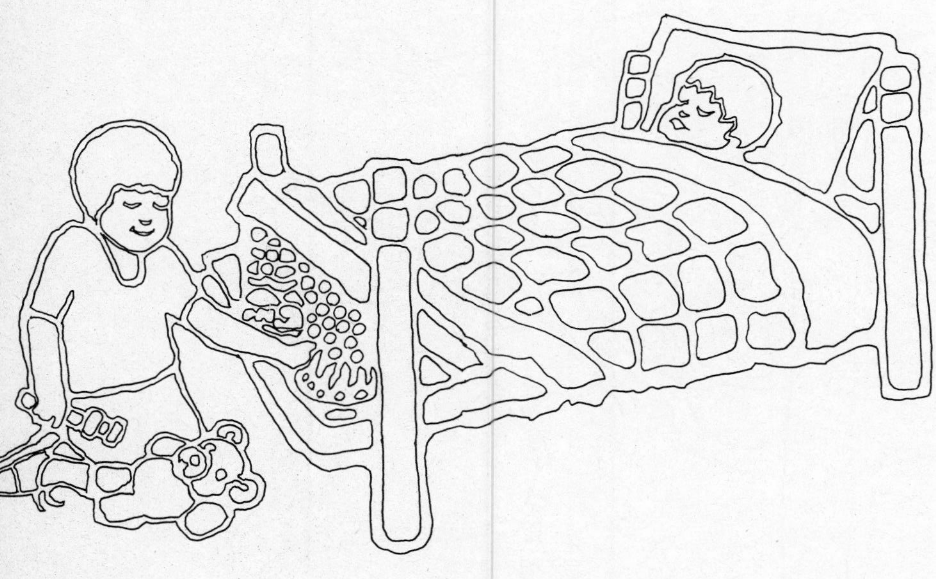

Minibook 17

Collections for Young Scholars™

Minibook

I tell Julia she is wrong.
Julia says that rude sisters
should bow and beg her royal pardon.

One night Dad read us a fairy tale.
It was The Princess and the Pea.
In the story, a queen tested a visitor.
The visitor said she was a real princess.
The queen put a pea in a bed.
The visitor tried to sleep on the bed.

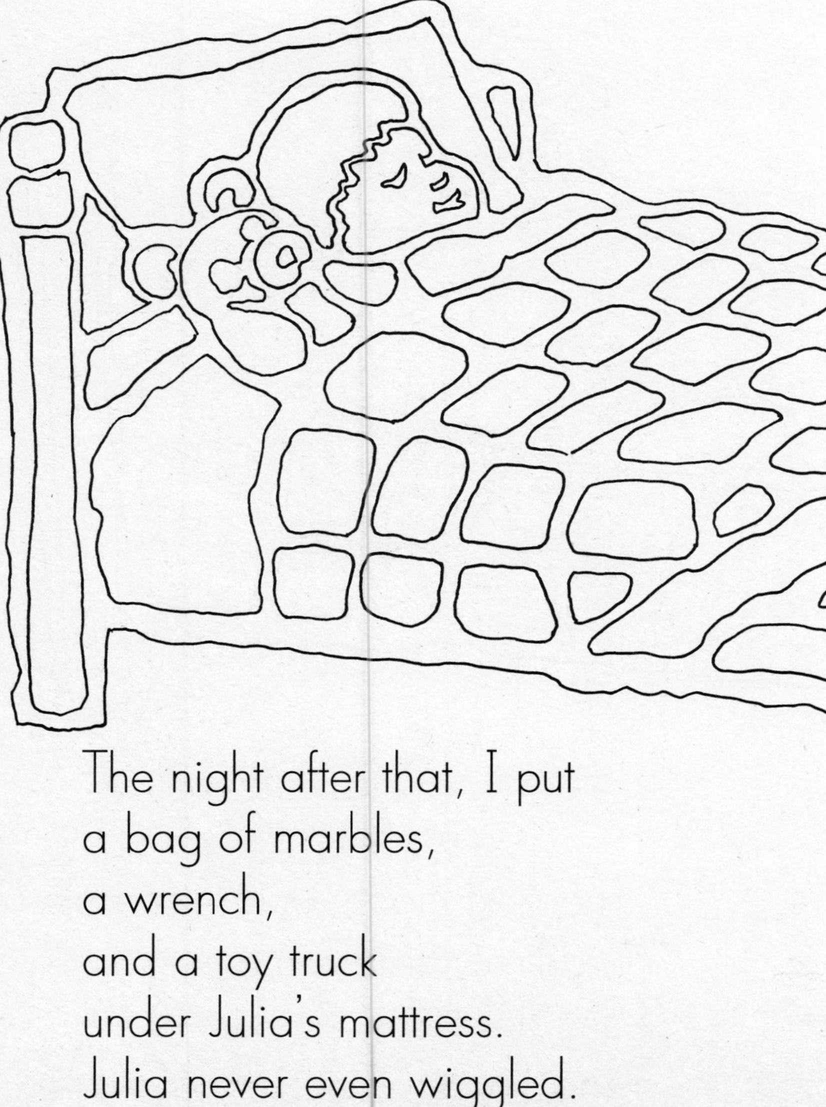

The night after that, I put
a bag of marbles,
a wrench,
and a toy truck
under Julia's mattress.
Julia never even wiggled.

The visitor could not sleep.
She felt something hard in the bed.
Only a real princess could have felt
a single pea in such a bed!

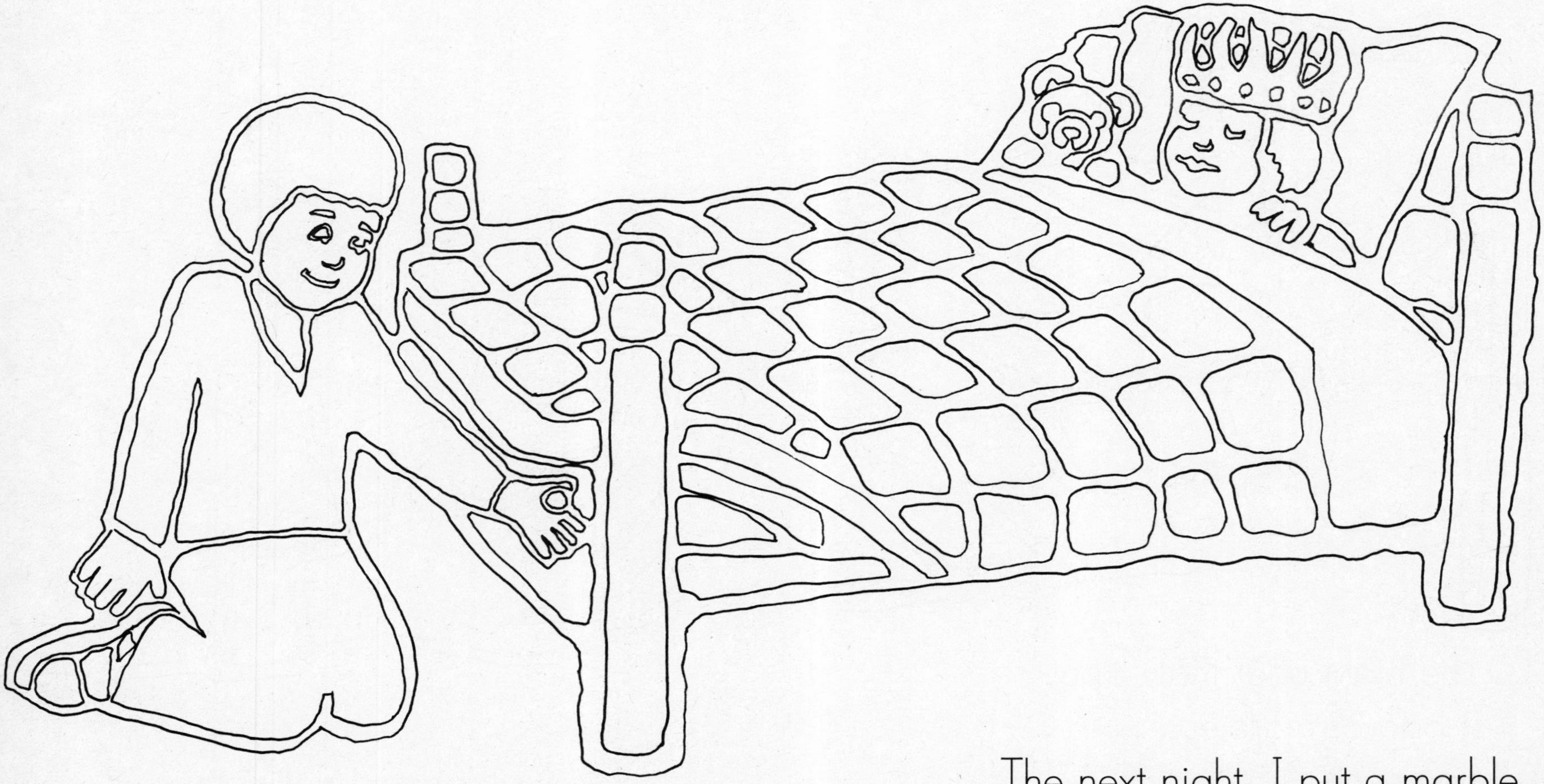

The story of the princess and the pea
gave me an idea.

The next night, I put a marble
under my sister's mattress.
She never felt a tickle.
She slept like a baby all night.

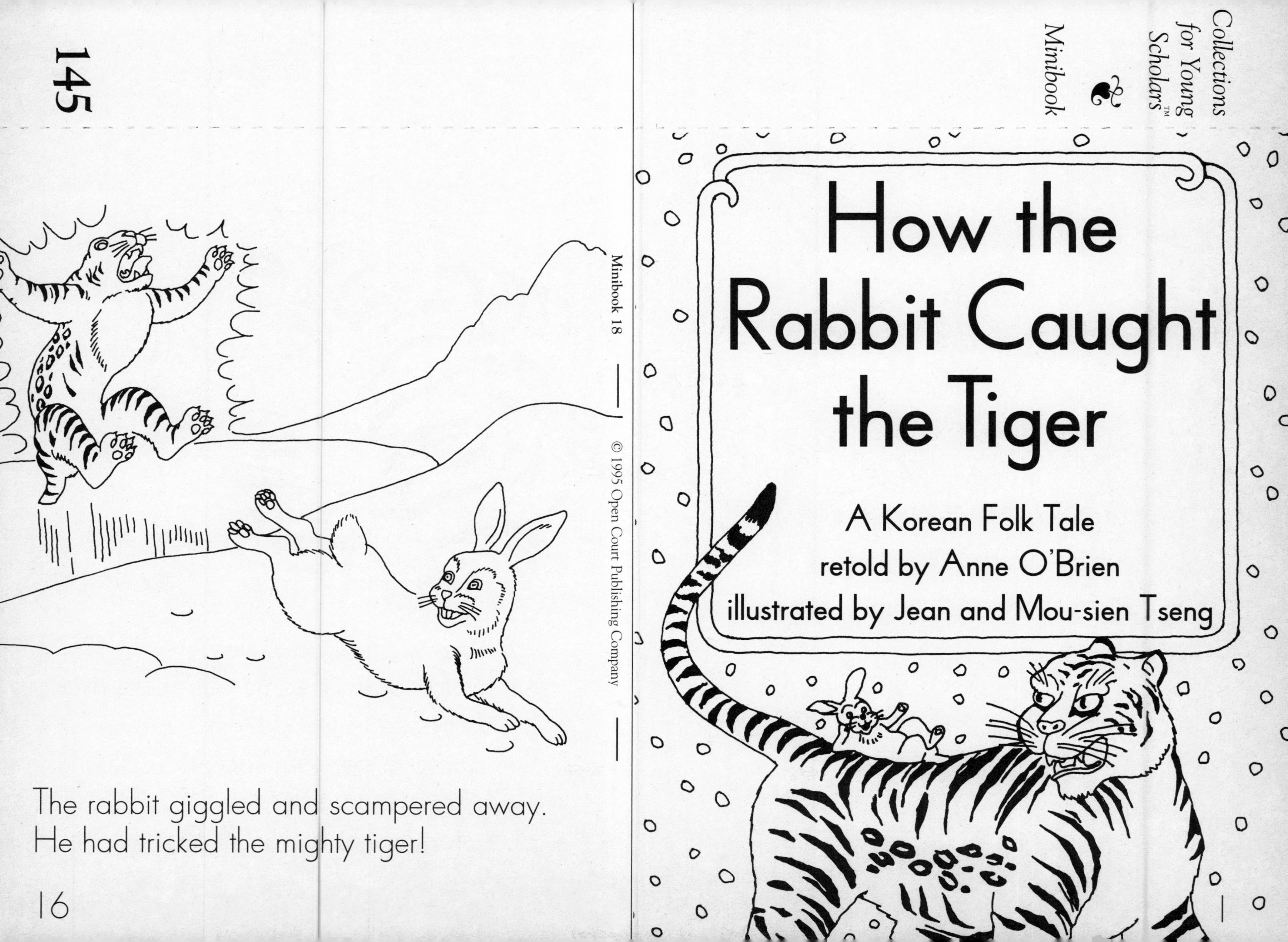

The rabbit giggled and scampered away. He had tricked the mighty tiger!

Minibook 18

How the Rabbit Caught the Tiger

A Korean Folk Tale

retold by Anne O'Brien

illustrated by Jean and Mou-sien Tseng

Collections for Young Scholars™

Minibook

The tiger pulled and pulled,
but his tail did not come out of the river.
It was frozen in the ice!
"I'm going to get you, rabbit!"
roared the angry tiger.
But he could not budge at all.

Collections for Young Scholars™

Minibook

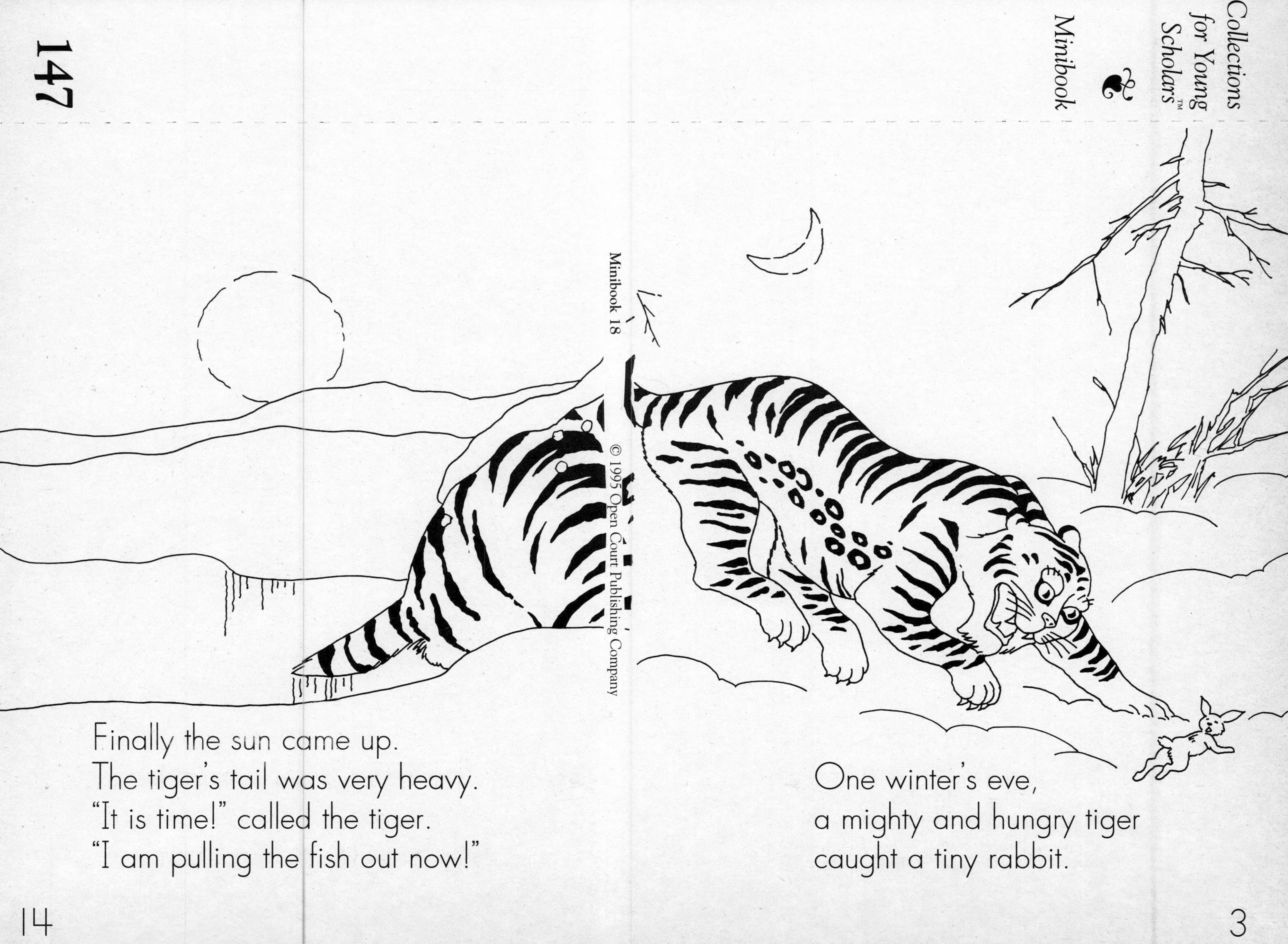

Finally the sun came up.
The tiger's tail was very heavy.
"It is time!" called the tiger.
"I am pulling the fish out now!"

Minibook 18

One winter's eve,
a mighty and hungry tiger
caught a tiny rabbit.

"Do not eat me!" cried the rabbit.
"I am too small to make a good meal.
If you let me go, I will show you
how to catch all the fish you can eat!"

The greedy tiger waited longer.
It grew colder and colder.
His tail grew heavier.

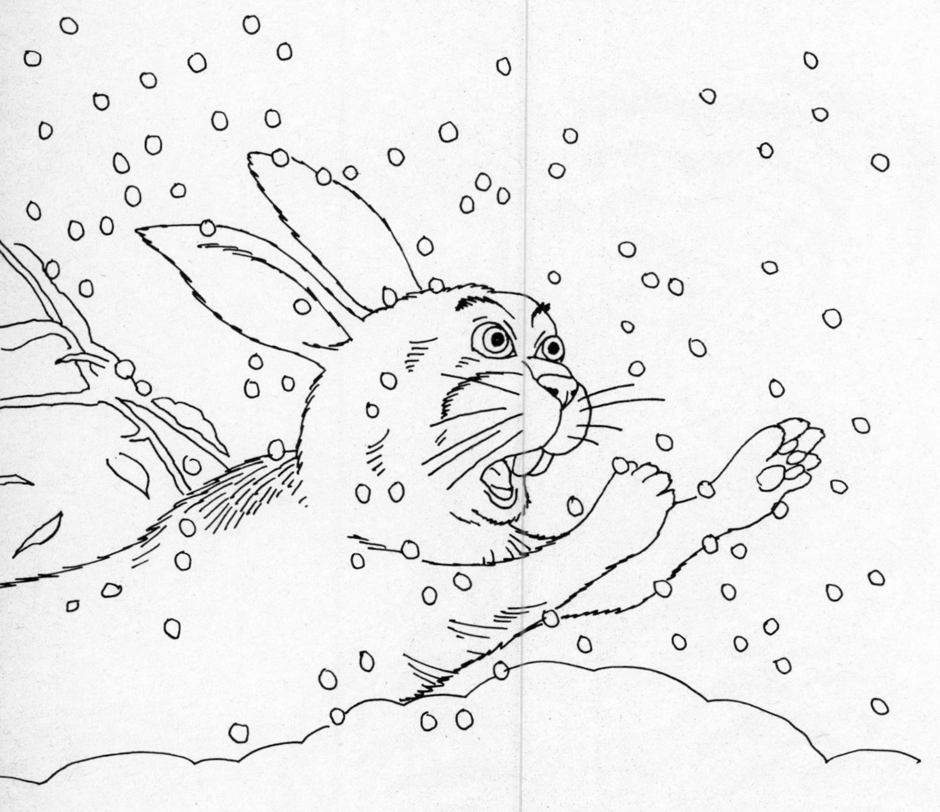

"Oh, no!" said the rabbit.
"If you wait until morning,
you will have more fish to eat!"

Minibook 18

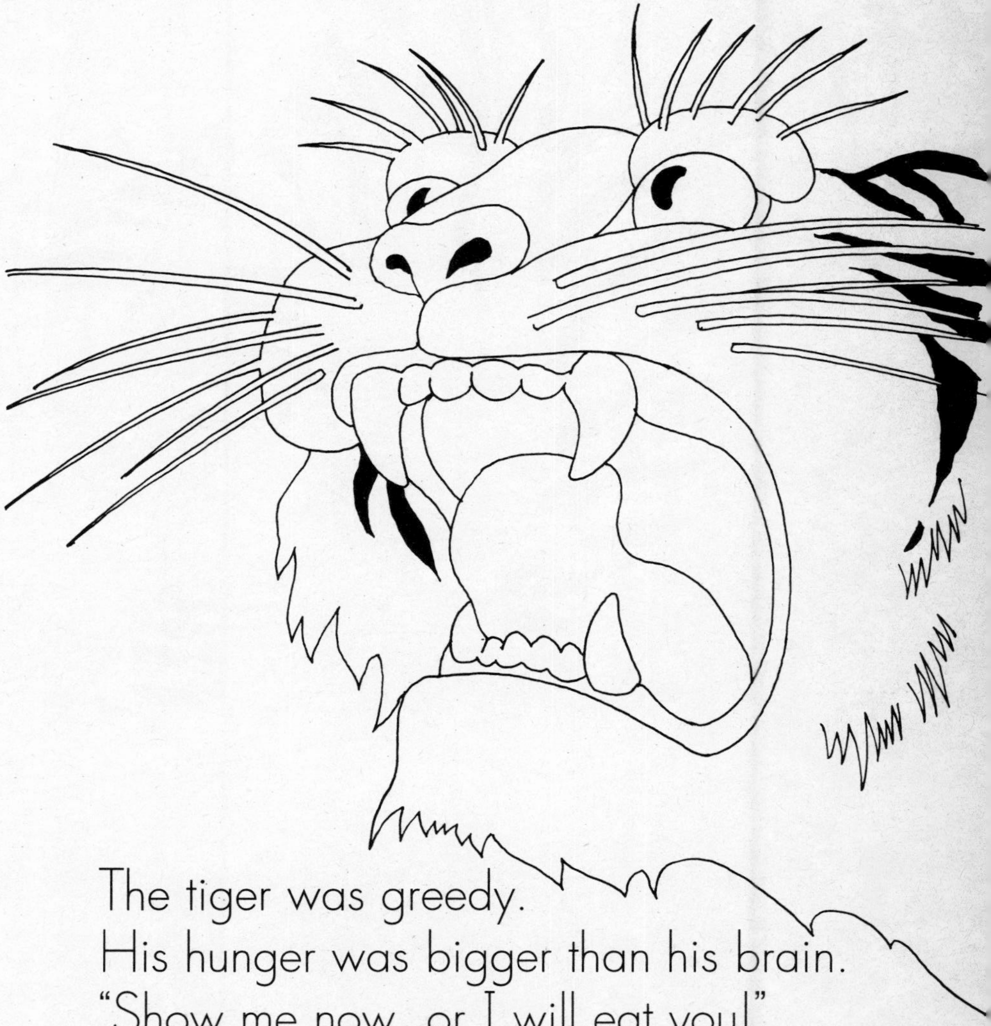

The tiger was greedy.
His hunger was bigger than his brain.
"Show me now, or I will eat you!"
he roared.
Then he let the rabbit go.

The rabbit led the tiger
down to the river.
"Put your tail in the water,"
said the rabbit.

"Is your tail getting heavy?"
called the rabbit.

"Oh, yes!" said the tiger.
"I must be catching lots of fish!
Should I pull my tail out now?

Minibook 18

"Now wait all night.
The fish will grab onto your tail.
Your tail will grow very heavy.
Then you can pull it out
and eat all the fish!"

"I'll stay close by," said the rabbit.
"I will let you know when
you have caught plenty of fish."
The rabbit climbed up the riverbank
and sat down to watch the tiger.

The tiger put his tail into the river.
He waited and waited.
It grew cold and dark.